18-550-30

A SHORT HISTORY
OF THE UNIVERSE

A SHORT HISTORY
OF THE UNIVERSE

THE STARS AND PLANETS:
THEIR BIRTH, EVOLUTION, NATURE

by Arthur S. Gregor

illustrated with drawings by Tom Funk
and photographs

THE MACMILLAN COMPANY, NEW YORK

COLLIER-MACMILLAN LIMITED, LONDON

For Laurie and George,
who set their sights
by the stars

FRONTISPIECE: *NGC 2403, a spiral nebula*
in the constellation Camelopardus.

Library of Congress catalog card number: 62-17333
First Printing
The Macmillan Company, New York
Collier-Macmillan Canada, Ltd., Toronto, Ontario
Printed in the United States of America

☆ IN an exciting story by H. G. Wells, "The Time Machine," the hero invents a machine in which he can travel in time just as men travel in space.

In his machine he goes back to ancient times, then to the days of the cavemen, to the coming of life on earth, and even to the beginning of the world. After his return out of the past to our century, he sets out for the world of the future.

Wells relied on his imagination to picture the world of the past and the future. In *A Short History of the Universe*, we too will go exploring in time. Though we will depend only on the work of modern astronomy, we will tell a far stranger story than any science-fiction writer ever imagined. ☆

CONTENTS

THE GALAXIES

Fifty Trillion Miles to the Dog Star
JOURNEY INTO SPACE   3

A Carousel of Stars
THE MILKY WAY   7

Where the Universe Ends
THE GALAXIES   10

The Universe Is a Lonely Place
SPACE, ALMOST EMPTY   13

The Universe Is Also Noisy
GAS, BLACK DUST, AND STARS   14

Our Nearest Star
THE SUN   17

The Death of the Stars
RED GIANTS, BLACK DWARFS, AND
SUPERNOVAS   23

How Did the Universe Begin?
HYDROGEN, GRAVITATION, AND
EXPANSION   27

The Universe Is Getting Bigger
THE RUNAWAY GALAXIES   29

A Birth Certificate for the Universe?
DATING OUR GALAXY   32

The Big Bang
THE FIRST ATOMIC EXPLOSION   37

A Birthday Every Day
CREATION AT ALL HOURS   40

Something Out of Nothing
WAS THE UNIVERSE ALWAYS HERE?   43

THE SOLAR SYSTEM

Invisible Wheel in the Sky
THE SOLAR SYSTEM   49

Planet of Endless Day and Endless Night
MERCURY   52

The Mystery Planet
VENUS   54

A Chance for Life
MARS   56

Flying Mountains
THE ASTEROIDS   59

Snowball in the Sky
JUPITER   60

Ring Around a Planet
SATURN 63

The Solar System's Outfield
URANUS, NEPTUNE, AND PLUTO 65

Hairy Stars and Shooting Stars
COMETS AND METEORS 67

A Message from Outer Space
METEORITES 72

How Did the Solar System Begin?
THE NEBULAR HYPOTHESIS 75

Did the Solar System Begin as an Accident?
COLLISIONS AND EXPLOSIONS 77

Out of a Cloud of Dust
BIRTH OF THE SUN AND PLANETS 79

Quick Planets and Lazy Sun
THE CRUCIAL TEST 81

Life on Other Worlds
TO FIND A SUN LIKE OURS 83

Man Is Not Alone in the Universe
OTHER WORLDS AND OTHER MEN 87

THE EARTH

A View from Another Planet
THE EARTH IN SPACE 93

A Lake of Iron
DEEP INSIDE THE EARTH 95

Solving a Jigsaw Puzzle
THE SURFACE OF THE EARTH   100

Sandpapering the Globe
EROSION SHAPES THE EARTH   105

Fountains of Life
AIR AND WATER   107

A World of the Dead
THE MOON   109

The First Time It Rained
HOW THE EARTH BEGAN   112

Neither Animal nor Plant
HOW LIFE CAME TO THE EARTH   115

The Chain of Life
MAN JOINS THE UNIVERSE   117

AFTERWORD   121

INDEX   125

Yerkes Observatory

THE GALAXIES

JOURNEY INTO SPACE

The universe lies all about us.

It is the ground at our feet and the heavens over our head. It is the cake baking in the oven and the cat purring in the corner. It is the shade tree along the street and the boy playing ball on the stoop.

It is the rain, the cloud that brings the rain, and the wind that sweeps it away. It is the sun, the moon, the planets, and the stars—and whatever it is that lies beyond the stars. The universe is here and everywhere. It was in the past, it is in the present, and will be in the future.

The universe is all and everything!

How did the universe come to be? When did it begin? How big is it? Where does it end?

What are the stars? Are there other worlds with life like ours?

To find what answers science can offer, let's take a journey into space.

Where are we starting from?

From a space platform called the earth. In the company of eight other planets of the solar system, our earth circles around the sun in a part of the heavens known as the Milky Way.

3

We will have to travel fast.

A supersonic plane flies at 700 miles an hour. A manned rocket whizzes around the earth at 16,000 miles an hour. But to overcome the gravitational hold that clamps all things to the surface of our globe, our spaceship will have to hit at least 25,000 miles an hour.

All right, there's the end of the countdown. With a zoom and a roar, we're off!

Rising up out of the sea of air that covers the earth, we go faster and faster. In a few minutes farms, roads, towns, even huge cities, vanish from sight. We can make out the great land masses and the ocean, but soon even they are gone. The earth shrinks, grows round, and becomes a great ball floating in space behind us.

Since the moon is only 250,000 miles from the earth, we're there in ten hours—supposing that we travel in a straight line —hardly time to get used to our spaceship.

We slip past the moon and set our course for the red planet, Mars, over 50 million miles away. A full three months go by before we arrive and are ready for the next leg in our journey to the biggest of all the planets, Jupiter. But Jupiter is 400 million miles from the earth, and even at 25,000 miles an hour, almost two years go by before we near the giant planet.

Luckily, we avoid running into the swarm of asteroids that inhabit this region of the sky. Long ago, we believe, there was another planet between Mars and Jupiter. Perhaps one day it smashed up, leaving behind the asteroid fragments that still dutifully circle the sun just as the parent planet once did.

Jupiter is a long trip, perhaps more than we bargained for. But since we've come so far, what about trying for the outer-most of all the planets that belong to our solar system: the mysterious and little-known Pluto.

We glide by Saturn with its rings (the most beautiful sight

4

in the heavens), Uranus and its five moons, and Neptune blanketed in ice and frozen gases.

Have you noticed that the sun has been getting smaller and smaller? Shortly it will be only a pinpoint of light in the darkened sky. It's hard to distinguish it from the stars.

Our magnificent sun, then, is only a star! Distance decides whether we call it *star* or *sun*. If our earth were close enough to another star, that star would become our sun.

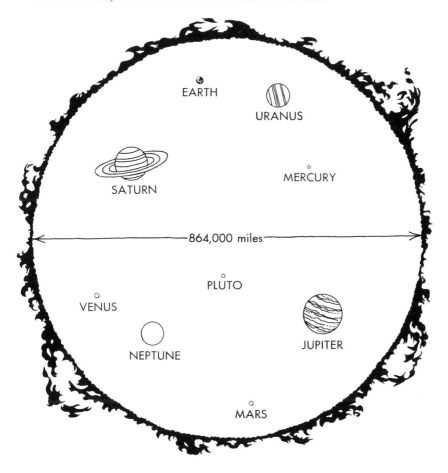

The sun is so huge that all the planets of the solar system could be stored inside it with plenty of room left over.

5

At long last we reach Pluto, the last stop on the planetary line. How long have we been on our way?

For twenty years. No wonder: Pluto is three and a half billion miles away from the earth.

Where to now?

The stars invite us. Why not aim for one of them? Let's say, Sirius, the Dog Star, one of our closest neighbors. You can easily see it on a winter's evening, the clearest, brightest star in the eastern sky. It looks as though it is just over the rooftops, and astronomers say it is only eight and a half light-years away.

But how far away is eight and a half light-years?

Let's see. We know that light travels at 186,000 miles a second. Glance up from the page you are reading for just three seconds and a beam of light will have had more than enough time to get to the moon and back. A little quick arithmetic tells us that if light travels 186,000 miles in one second, in one year it will have traveled 5,878 million miles: Multiply that by eight and a half!

Sirius may be shining brightly over the rooftops, but actually it is over 50 thousand billion miles away. Even at 25,000 miles an hour, we'd need 230,000 years to get to the Dog Star. Until we are ready to live at least that long, we'd better give up all hope of getting to Sirius—or to any of the other stars.

Suppose that by some miracle we could travel with the speed of light. Even then we wouldn't do much star-hopping. Only a dozen stars are within ten light-years of us, most are over a hundred light-years away, and many are thousands of light-years away.

Chances are that man will never set his foot one step beyond the planets. The vast distances of space are too much for him. If we are going to explore the universe, it can only be by means of the instruments of modern astronomy.

Our journey into space has barely begun.

THE MILKY WAY

Look up at the Milky Way on a clear night.

It seems as if a giant hand had flung granulated sugar across the sky. Now examine it through a small telescope and each grain of sugar becomes a separate star.

The Milky Way is a galaxy, or family, of stars. With your eye you should be able to take in about two thousand of them. But when you use your telescope, the number jumps to over one million. Actually the number of stars in the Milky Way goes into the billions.

The Milky Way looks crowded, and many of the stars seem to be touching, but there is no danger that they will ever collide. Billions of miles separate them from each other. The stars keep their distance.

If you should imagine the stars shrunk to the size of tennis balls, then the distance between them would average 4,000 miles. The "crowded" Milky Way is mostly empty space.

How large is our sun compared to the other stars? Not very big at all. In fact, quite small.

It is surprising but true that our glorious sun is only a midget among stars. Some stars are hundreds of times larger than the sun. And then there are the colossal "red giant" stars, which are so big that one of them, placed in the position of the sun, would easily swallow Mercury, Venus, and even the earth. We'd be stewing within our new sun. Just as well that our sun is small.

Another great surprise about the sun is that it is located inside the Milky Way. Since our earth is close to the sun, we also are inside the Milky Way.

But how can we be inside the Milky Way when we can look up at it any night in the year?

Actually we are not looking *up* at it, but looking *out* of it. We are surrounded on all sides by the other stars of the Milky Way, and we are peeping from the inside out.

What does the Milky Way look like from the outside? It's hard to imagine. If we had to spend our life indoors, we'd have a difficult time getting to know what the outside of our house looked like.

What would we see if we *could* look down on the Milky Way?

A vast collection of stars shaped like a pancake, a pancake 600 million billion miles across and 60 million billion miles deep! Attached to its sides we would see extra portions called spiral arms. Looking very closely we'd notice that our sun is located in one of these spiral arms. We are not in the center but in one of the suburbs of our galaxy.

Why do the stars seem so packed together when we look up at the Milky Way from the earth? Because we are peering through the length of the pancake. The stars thin out when we glance to either side of the Milky Way because we are viewing the top and bottom of the pancake.

Let's get back to our perch high above the Milky Way.

Our galaxy is not still! It is turning round and round like a giant carousel. And on this giant carousel, the stars, the sun, the planets and their satellites, and our own earth are all spinning around and around. The entire galaxy and all its parts are in constant and dizzying motion.

We think we are going pretty fast when our car hits "seventy" on the parkway. And yet on our galactic merry-go-round we are doing a million miles every two hours, and without a bump, jolt, or jounce—the smoothest ride in the universe.

In addition to our movement of 500,000 miles an hour on

Our galaxy, the Milky Way, as it might look if we could get billions of miles above it. ("Galaxy" comes from the Greek word *gala*, which means "milk.") The dot is our sun, around which the earth and the other planets circle.

the galaxy, we are also swinging around the sun at 68,000 miles an hour, and at the same time the earth is spinning like a top at over 1,000 miles an hour at the equator. Every day of our lives we do almost 14 million miles. We really are traveling!

Our sun and the other stars of the Milky Way have taken the carousel ride only twenty times since the day of their creation. But that should not surprise us. Each round trip takes 200 million years.

9

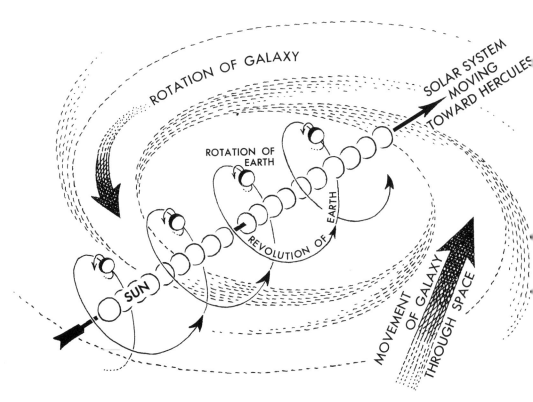

ROTATION OF GALAXY

SOLAR SYSTEM MOVING TOWARD HERCULES

ROTATION OF EARTH

REVOLUTION OF EARTH

MOVEMENT OF GALAXY THROUGH SPACE

SUN

Even when we stand perfectly still, we are doing a lot of moving. We are spinning with the earth as it whirls about on its axis. The earth, together with the rest of the planets, is revolving about the sun. The sun is rushing toward the constellation Hercules at 12 miles a second. At the same time the entire galaxy, of which the sun is only one small star, is whirling through space as though it were a platter tossed by a giant hand.

WHERE THE UNIVERSE ENDS

THE GALAXIES

Is the Milky Way the whole universe?

Let us imagine that we could get to Sirius and from there go on and on from star to star, leaping across the vast distances that separate them. Would we ever come to the end of the Milky Way?

Yes, there would come a time when the stars would thin out, and then there would be no more. Before us would stretch an immense black emptiness.

Would this then be the *end* of the universe?

Until about forty years ago, astronomers believed that it would be, that the Milky Way was the entire universe. In it were our earth, our sun and its solar system, Sirius, the North Star, the Great Dipper, and the other constellations: in all, about 125 billion stars plus their planets and satellites.

But in 1923 Dr. Edwin Hubble turned the new 100-inch telescope of Mount Wilson Observatory on a curious cloud known as the nebula in Andromeda. Photographed through the Mount Wilson telescope, this bit of fluff turned into a great collection of stars. Dr. Hubble estimated that it was at least 750,000 light-years away (it is really more than twice that distance). If it was that far away, then it must be at least as large as the Milky Way.

It was, in fact, another galaxy. Our family of stars was not alone in space.

And when he turned his giant telescope to other sections of the heavens, Dr. Hubble came upon not one or two but thousands of other galaxies. Cradled within the outline of the Great Dipper, for example, he counted more than three hundred star clusters. Space thronged with galaxies and each one contained billions of stars. The universe did not end at the boundaries of the Milky Way.

How far does it continue?

The famous 200-inch Hale telescope of Palomar Observatory, the world's most powerful, can carry us four billion light-years, or 24,000,000,000,000,000,000,000,000 miles, away from the earth. And still it encounters fresh galaxies.

And beyond that?

Why suppose that the universe comes to an end just because

11

we cannot see any further? The more we learn about the universe the larger it grows.

Until about five hundred years ago men were certain that the universe was centered right here on earth. The sky, in which the stars and the planets were set like electric light bulbs, was only a great roof over our heads. The sun was a globe that conveniently slid across the sky once a day to furnish us with heat and light.

Then astronomers like Copernicus and Galileo revealed that our earth was really not the universe. We were only one planet of a number of planets that moved about the sun. The sun itself was only one of an innumerable number of stars. The universe did not stop at the sky, but stretched out into space in all directions.

At the beginning of the nineteenth century, William Herschel turned a new telescope, which he and his sister Caroline had built, to the Milky Way. He realized that all of its many stars make up one great, lens-shaped cluster, or galaxy. Then, far beyond our system of stars, he noticed hazy patches of light, or nebulae, some of which could be resolved into groups of stars.

In our own century we have found out that even the magnificent Milky Way is only one of many, many galaxies, only a shred of the greater universe that goes on and on. No matter how far we travel we come across no high fences marked: *Halt! Universe Ends Here! Go No Farther!*

Hubble's discovery of the galaxy in Andromeda, or M 31 as the astronomers labeled it, is one of the great events in the history of science. The universe is far grander than man ever imagined even in his wildest dreams. Even the four-billion light-year universe of the Mount Palomar telescope is itself only a tiny island in the infinite ocean of space.

SPACE, ALMOST EMPTY

There is order and organization in the heavens—the stars, as fast as they are moving, are bound together. Instead of scattering pell-mell, they stay within their own galaxy.

Some of the galaxies look like Fourth-of-July pinwheels, others are shaped like saucers, and still others like footballs. Some have no particular shape at all.

We don't actually know what the galaxies look like right now. Because they are so far away, their light takes a long time to reach us. We see them, therefore, as they were millions of years ago.

Suppose a galaxy blew up tonight. More than a million years would go by before we knew anything about it. What we see in the sky today is a picture of what happened a long time ago. When we look out in space, we look back in time!

Just as stars cluster together in galaxies, so galaxies huddle close to each other in local groups. But not too close, for even the closest huddlers are over a million light-years apart.

Our Milky Way keeps company with eighteen other galaxies, including M 31 and the two Magellanic Clouds.

The Magellanic Clouds were first seen by Magellan when he sailed into the South Pacific on his journey around the world. They are irregular ragbags of stars in the constellation of the Southern Cross, which you should be able to see without a telescope whenever you are south of the equator.

Our local group of galaxies reaches four million light-years across the heavens. M 31 holds one side of this region and the Milky Way stands guard at the other. Surrounding our local group is empty space, vast areas of darkness stretching in all directions. Far off in the darkness is another local group and then darkness again, and so on and on through the universe.

Huge as the local groups and their galaxies are, there is one thing far, far greater—space itself. The galaxies occupy only a tiny part of space. They dwell in almost complete emptiness. Put them, with all their stars, together in one heap and it is only a glowing coal in an immeasurable and unexplored cave.

The universe is a lonely place.

THE UNIVERSE IS ALSO NOISY

GAS, BLACK DUST, AND STARS

Have you a sharp pair of eyes? Then after supper on a clear January or February night, see if you can make out the galaxy in Andromeda. One and one-half million light-years away, it is the farthest object any human being has succeeded in seeing without a telescope.

Don't expect another Milky Way, though. As far as you can see, it will only be a wisp of smoke near the star Nu in the constellation of Andromeda. But photograph it with the Schmidt telescopic camera and it becomes another island universe.

M 31, the galaxy in Andromeda, bears a startling resemblance to our own galaxy. Though a little larger, it has the same arrangement of stars and the same kind of spiral arms. To someone in M 31, the Milky Way would look very much the way the Andromeda galaxy looks to us.

Just as in the Milky Way, the older, reddish stars are in the center, and the younger, blueish stars are in the spiral arms. Our sun, though a yellow star, is still young, and if we were in M 31, we'd be entitled to a place in one of its arms.

Like the Milky Way, M 31 also has two companion galaxies trailing after it. Our companion galaxies are the Magellanic Clouds. Only 150,000 light-years from us, they may be too close to be considered independent star families. Photographed from another galaxy, they would look as though they were part of the Milky Way.

When we study M 31, we may imagine we are seeing our own galaxy. Unable to leave our own house, we've gotten to know what it looks like from the outside by gazing out the window at its twin across the road.

Astronomers, however, have noticed one strange difference between the two galaxies: The center of the Andromeda cluster, so many light-years away, is easily seen. The center of our own galaxy, close as we are to it, is hidden.

"Why," they asked, "can't our telescopes get through to the heart of our own island universe?"

Even without a telescope you can see that parts of the Milky Way are not very bright. For so many millions of stars there are a surprising number of gray and black patches. Some sections are quite dark.

"There must be stars in those dark regions," the astronomers said. "But we just can't see them. Some kind of smoke or smog must be blotting them out."

It was a good guess. Observation of stars that were only partly blacked out showed that interstellar space is not as empty as we had always thought. It is teeming with a black dust, a kind of heavenly rubbish made up of small drops of ice, carbon, and calcium. This dust shuts off our view of the stars in the center of the galaxy.

The universe is orderly, but it certainly is not tidy.

But how can we be certain of the existence of stars we cannot see? For the same reason that we can be certain of the presence of a ship in the fog—by the sound it makes.

Many of the stars are talking to us. Radio waves generated by these invisible stars pass through interstellar dust the way the sound of a ship's horn passes through fog. Radio telescopes

Radio telescopes allow us to explore portions of the heavens now hidden by interstellar gas and dust. They can penetrate regions of space that lie far beyond the range of the most powerful optical telescope.

here on earth—like gigantic ears—catch these waves, although they cannot yet pinpoint the stars which generate them.

Radio telescopes discovered something else in space that we had known very little about: the presence of a cool hydrogen gas, billions of times thinner than the air we breathe. This gas gives off no light and so can not be seen. But like the invisible stars, it gave itself away by chattering and beeping on a wave length of 21.1 centimeters.

Outer space is noisy!

THE SUN

What makes the difference between the glare of the sun and the pinpoint sparkle of a star?

Only the distance from which we see them. The sun is the star nearest us. What we learn about our sun, therefore, can help unlock the secrets of stars in the farthest reaches of the heavens.

The sun is one of the smaller stars, but compared to our planet it is tremendous. It is so large that a million earths could easily rattle around inside it.

The sun's huge mass gives it enormous gravitational pull. On its surface a 100-pound boy would tip the scales at 3,000 pounds.

The earth and the other planets have no light of their own. Like the moon they can only reflect the light the sun sends them. The sun, on the other hand, manufactures its own energy. Only a tiny part of it, less than one billionth, reaches us here on earth. But it's enough to keep this globe warm and supply the needs of all growing things.

All green plants and trees, all animal life, all the coal, oil, and natural gas locked under the surface of the earth owe their existence to the energy the sun has poured onto our planet for many millions of years.

You might suppose that after ages and ages of supplying light and heat for the earth and all the other planets, the sun would begin to peter out. Yet the temperature on the surface of the sun today registers a blistering 10,000 degrees F. Quite a bit of heat when you recall that water boils at 212 degrees F.

The whole sun is a glowing gas. The heat is so intense that nothing solid can exist close to it even for a moment. Get

17

within 100,000 miles of the sun in the strongest lead-and-asbestos suit, and you too become a glowing gas.

Hot as the surface is, it's icy compared to the inside, which goes up to an unimaginable 25 million degrees F. If a giant hand ripped the interior of the sun open and the heat spilled out into space, Mercury and Venus would flare up and the earth itself would turn to ashes in a few hours.

At 25 million degrees even light itself is snuffed out. The inside of the sun must be pitch black. Energy exists there only in the form of X-rays.

As these X-rays make their way to the surface of the sun, they cool off and turn into the sunlight we enjoy on earth. A

The sun's energy enables green leaves to transform carbon dioxide and water into living plant tissue. Three hundred million years ago, the debris of giant tree ferns and other plants was slowly converted into fossil fuels such as coal, gas, and oil.

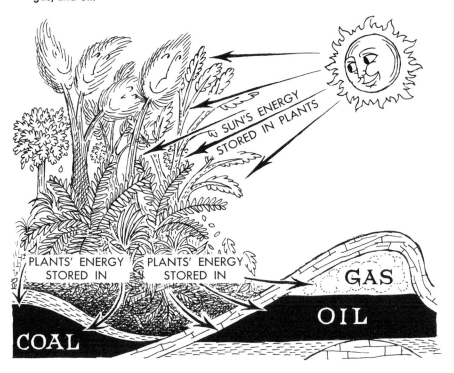

lovely June day is a continuation of the dangerous rays that began their life in the heart of the sun.

Where does the sun get all its energy from?

Let's imagine that it comes from coal, the very best and hardest coal. In three thousand years the coal would be burned up and the sun would be a mass of cinders. Still, the sun has been shining for billions of years. It is certainly not coal or any ordinary fuel that the sun has been using.

What can burn that long and that fiercely?

The answer is that the sun, like the other stars, gets its energy from a thermonuclear reaction, just as a hydrogen bomb does.

Most of the sun is hydrogen. The terrific heat in the sun's center forces hydrogen atoms to fuse, or join together, and form helium. Four hydrogen atoms (H) turn into one helium atom (He) and at the same time release tremendous quantities of energy (E).

"4 H = 1 He + E" is the formula that keeps the universe warm.

But Nature gives nothing away. In return for her energy, the sun loses five million tons of its weight every second. Try figuring out what that comes to—in an hour? a day? a year? a thousand years?

Surely the sun is growing smaller and smaller and will finally disappear altogether.

Not at all, at least not for a long time. The sun is so huge that it will be many millions of years before it will be compelled to take in its belt.

But the sun is burning countless tons of hydrogen it can never get back. Should it not cool off, then, just the way a campfire does as the fuel is used up?

The answer is hardly what we'd expect. As the sun loses hydrogen, it gets hotter, not cooler!

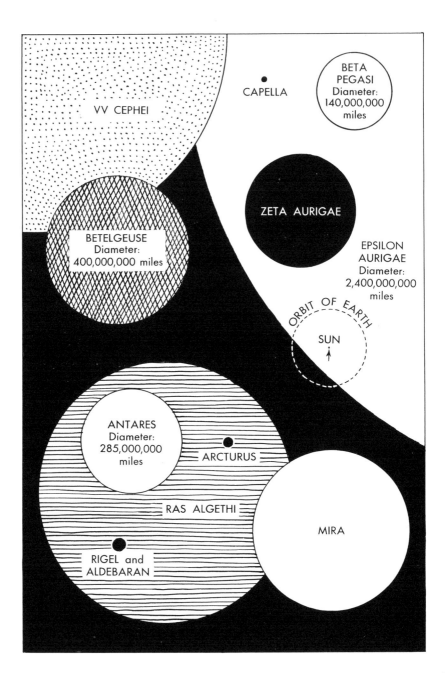

Compared to the giant stars, our sun is only a dot in space. Some of the giants are so huge that they could fill all the space within the earth's orbit. And then there are the supergiants, such as Epsilon Aurigae, that are many times larger.

This sounds so fantastic that perhaps we ought to get away from the sun for a while and look in on the interior of our own planet.

We know that the temperature at the bottom of a mine is higher than the temperature at the surface. In fact, the deeper you go into the earth, the higher the temperature rises. Far beneath the surface the heat is great enough to melt stone. The lava that spews out of the mouth of a volcano is molten rock.

What causes such tremendous heat? The pressure of the earth itself.

On the surface of the earth, the pressure of the atmosphere is one ton to one square foot. Twenty-five miles down, the total pressure is ten tons. Two thousand miles down, it turns metal into a molasses. At the center of the earth, the squeeze is so great that iron runs like liquid. And as the pressure increases, so does the temperature.

Now let's return to the sun. The sun is so much bigger than the earth, and its squeeze, therefore, is so much greater. At the center of the sun, the temperature is high enough to keep a thermonuclear reaction going continuously. Every second, hydrogen is being turned into helium and energy.

What happens, then, as the sun's hydrogen is used up? The sun "caves in" bit by bit and shrinks in size. The shrinking increases the internal squeeze, the squeeze increases the temperature, and the sun is hotter than ever before.

What can we say about the future of the sun?

But *before* we say anything more, we ought to stop for a word of caution. What astronomers say about the evolution of the stars and the sun can be no more than informed guesses. Man has not been around long enough to make up any kind of accurate stellar timetable.

The sun will at first grow smaller and smaller and hotter and hotter. Today it is a fairly warm, yellow star. Someday it will

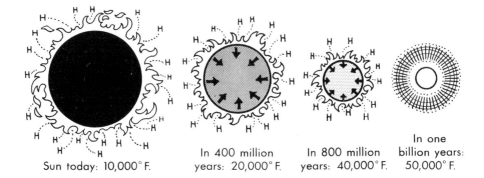

Sun today: 10,000° F.   In 400 million years: 20,000° F.   In 800 million years: 40,000° F.   In one billion years: 50,000° F.

As the sun loses hydrogen, it collapses a little. The shrinking increases the internal pressure, which, in turn, raises the temperature. The result is that, like many of the other stars, the more energy the sun loses, the hotter it gets.

become one of the hottest stars in the heavens, a blue-white star with a surface temperature of 50,000 degrees F.

When that happens the temperature of the earth will go well above the boiling point of water, which means that life will be impossible. But let's not get panicky. All this is not scheduled to happen for another billion years, and before then we should have plenty of opportunity to work out some sort of world-wide air-conditioning system.

But can the sun keep on squandering its mass forever? Won't the time come when the sun will have used up all of its hydrogen so that it becomes a burned-out star, a dead body floating in the sky without light or heat or any other kind of energy?

Don't be impatient. That time will come too. But long before that day arrives, the sun will have passed through the second and perhaps the strangest part of its story. It will join the company of the red giants.

RED GIANTS, BLACK DWARFS AND SUPERNOVAS

Of one thing we can be certain in this mysterious universe of ours: Everything changes. Everything is subject to evolution.

Even stars change. They change their color, their brightness, even their size. They are born, they go through youth and middle age, they become old, and they die.

Today our star, the sun, is a mere teen-ager. A billion years from now it will become a youth, smaller than it is today but making up in brightness and in energy what it lacks in size. It will be one of the most prominent stars in the Milky Way.

Three billion years from now, it will have reached middle age. The hydrogen in its core will have turned into helium, and at this point it will stop shrinking. It will begin to swell until it becomes a red giant like Antares, Mira, or Betelgeuse.

As our aging sun gets bigger and bigger, it will creep down into space and swallow, first, Mercury, then Venus, then the earth, then . . .

But why go on? Long before then, the earth—together with all its air-conditioning systems—will have become a mass of flaming gases deep within the raging furnace of the giant sun.

We can only speculate as to what can happen to a red giant star. We suppose that the time must come when the sun will have used up most of its fuel, and then it will begin to collapse all over again. Once again the internal squeezing will send the pressure up, and once again the sun will grow hotter and hotter. Its dull red color will become bright red, the bright red will become white, and the white will become blue.

At last, after another half-billion years or so, the sun will

23

have lost its very last ounce of fuel. Then it will become a white dwarf star not much bigger than the earth but a million times heavier. Within a few million years it will turn black, its light and heat gone forever.

The sun will be a black dwarf accompanied through the heavens by the few outer planets it failed to swallow in an earlier and brighter age.

Our galaxy probably contains only one dead dwarf to every twelve living stars. Can this possibly mean that our galaxy is rather young—since its cemeteries are not yet crowded with dead stars?

Does the fate of our sun await all the stars?

Perhaps. There is a principle in science which says that certain physical changes can go in one direction only. For example, what would happen if you placed a pot of boiling water on a cake of ice? Simple enough: The water would gradually become lukewarm and the ice would melt.

But can you make the change go the other way? If you placed a pot of lukewarm water in a puddle of melted ice, it would never become a pot of boiling water on a cake of ice. In other words, energy flows in one direction only.

So it may be with the stars. The flow of energy in space is largely one-way. The stars contain only a certain amount of energy, and one day all of it will be gone. One by one, the stars will be transformed into black dwarfs. One by one, their light will go out, and the bright firmament will become darker and darker until finally the stars will be gone from sight. Across the blacked-out heavens will float, unseen and unheard, countless galaxies of dead stars, like a funeral procession.

Sounds pretty gloomy, doesn't it? So let's end this chapter on a slightly more cheerful note.

Not every star is slated to become a black dwarf. A few are going to put on the most thrilling show in all the heavens and end their days as supernovas.

24

What is a supernova?

We know that as a heavenly body shrinks, it begins to spin. Some very hot stars are spinning at a rate of ten million miles an hour.

Caught between the pressure in its interior and the speed on its surface, such a star must inevitably explode. It blows up with the brilliance of a billion stars; sometimes it becomes brighter than its own galaxy. And its gases rush out and fill all of the neighboring space.

The first supernova we know anything about was recorded by Chinese astronomers way back in 1054 A.D. Appropriately enough, the date was July 4th!

Today, nine hundred years later, we can still see the remnants of that titanic explosion. Its gases now extend 35 trillion miles across the sky, and they are still expanding. You can see this supernova in the constellation of Taurus. It is called the

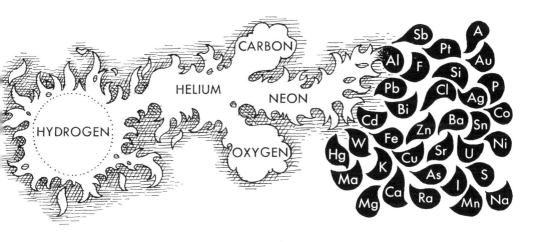

The elements are created in the furnace of the stars. A star probably starts out as pure hydrogen. By means of nuclear fusion, the hydrogen is converted into helium, which is then transformed into carbon, oxygen, and neon. The neon, in turn, becomes magnesium, silicon, phosphorus, calcium, iron, nickel, and all the other elements. Ninety-nine percent of the universe is made of hydrogen and helium, with hydrogen far in the lead.

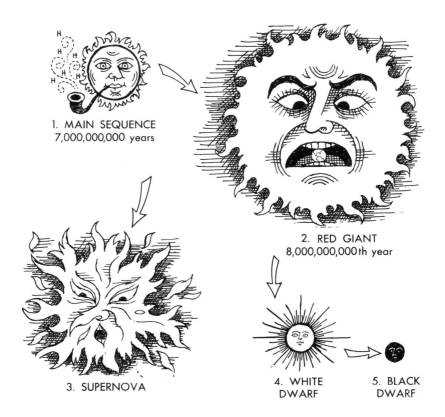

1. MAIN SEQUENCE
7,000,000,000 years

2. RED GIANT
8,000,000,000th year

3. SUPERNOVA

4. WHITE DWARF

5. BLACK DWARF

Stars differ in size, color, brightness, temperature, and chemical composition. Such differences indicate that stars evolve from one stage to another. Here is a rough suggestion as to the future of a star like our sun:

1. During its youth, which lasts, let's say, about seven billion years, a star is said to be in the main sequence, emitting vast amounts of energy into space through thermonuclear reaction. Our sun is a main-sequence star.

2. By its eight billionth year the star has consumed all the hydrogen in its hot central core. Since the hydrogen has been replaced by helium, the star expands enormously and becomes a red giant, burning up the closest planets and then consuming them.

3. But not every star gets to be a red giant. Some, torn between their spin and their internal pressure, explode and become supernovas like the Crab Nebula.

4. The colossal red giants eventually collapse and become white dwarfs, no larger than a large planet such as Saturn. Their supply of fuel is gone, and their material is packed so tight that a pinch of it weighs hundreds of tons.

5. The end comes when every last drop of energy is drained from the white dwarf. The star floats about unseen and unheard, a black dwarf.

Crab Nebula, and from the earth it looks no bigger than a dime, despite its size.

Another famous supernova was recorded by the Danish astronomer Tycho Brahe in 1572. It could easily be seen in broad daylight and for several days shone brighter than the planet Venus. Within a few years, however, it faded away. The next supernova was seen just thirty-two years later by the famous German astronomer Johannes Kepler.

What are the chances of seeing a supernova?

Not so good. In almost a thousand years these three are the only ones that have been observed with the naked eye. But astronomers believe that they occur fairly frequently, and if we keep our telescopes peeled on distant galaxies, we stand a good chance of seeing at least one a year.

HOW DID THE UNIVERSE BEGIN?

HYDROGEN, GRAVITATION, AND EXPANSION

We are now ready for the riddle that has kept men thinking and wondering through the ages.

How did this universe of countless galaxies, stars, and planets begin? Was there a certain time when it began or has it been here for all time? How did it get started?

The storytellers who spun the first legends around the campfire, the medicine men who sought the favor of the spirits of the wood, the holy saints and sages who founded the great religions of the world—all have tried to tell us what the beginning was like.

Now it is the turn of science.

Right off we have to admit that, unlike the others, we are not certain. Science refuses to say anything is true unless there is proof, and at the present time we have no real proof of what happened.

No scientist was present at the first moment of existence or for billions of years after. It all occurred before the earth and the sun were born, and before the stars took their place in the sky—a good long time ago.

All that science can offer us is a theory, a kind of informed guess based on whatever clues we have.

A detective enters a room, he looks around for evidence and then questions the witnesses. On the basis of what he sees and hears, he reconstructs what happened a few hours or days before.

The astronomer is also a detective except that he has much the tougher job. He can call no witnesses. On the basis of a few shreds of evidence, he must reconstruct what happened billions of years ago.

Don't be surprised if the scientists come up with more than one answer. Their disagreement will give you a chance to sit on the jury and make up your own mind. You may wish to accept one of the theories we'll talk about or you may wish to accept none of them.

What clues do we have?

Clue Number One is the presence of hydrogen throughout the universe. It is the most abundant of all the elements, the fuel that burns on all the stars. Without it, the universe would become cold and lifeless in a few years.

Hydrogen also floats in space between the stars. There it's so thin that in ten gallons of space you'd detect just one lone atom of hydrogen; we'd call that a near-perfect vacuum. Yet thin as this interstellar gas is, the total amount of it is amazing. Because the universe is so vast, this superfine gas outweighs, many times over, all the stars and all the planets combined.

Clue Number Two is gravitation. Gravitation is the holding

power that tends to keep all things together. We are held to the earth, the earth is held to the sun, the sun is held to the Milky Way, and the Milky Way is held to a cluster of galaxies that we call the local group.

The order we see in the universe is due in good part to the power of gravitation.

Our third and last clue is so strange that when astronomers came across it for the first time, they could not believe their senses. We know the universe is enormous. The amazing thing is that it's getting bigger.

In other words, it is expanding!

THE UNIVERSE IS GETTING BIGGER

THE RUNAWAY GALAXIES

Suppose you returned to your own neighborhood after having been away for a time.

The houses just across the street that you remember are now a quarter of a mile away. The houses that used to be a little way down the street are now three miles off. And as for the houses that once stood on the edge of your community, they are so far off you can no longer see them. Your old town is blowing up to gigantic size. You might think you were going mad.

You can imagine, then, how scientists felt when they discovered that the *universe* is getting bigger. Not houses but tremendous clusters of stars are flying off in every direction.

To picture what is happening, paste tiny bits of paper to a balloon. Now blow it up. As you do, you will notice that the papers move apart from each other.

The universe is a kind of ever-expanding balloon. The distance between the galaxies, like the distance between the bits of paper, is continually increasing. Each galaxy, however, like each bit of paper, remains the same size. The force of gravitation within each galaxy prevents the stars from flying away from the other stars in the cluster.

Seeing all the other galaxies moving away from our Milky Way, you may get the idea that we've suddenly become the most unpopular cluster of stars in the entire universe.

Not at all. Make your home on any galaxy and you'll find the other galaxies flying from you. *Every* galaxy is moving away from every other galaxy. Every galaxy is giving itself more elbow room. Space is becoming emptier—and lonelier.

Now how can we tell that galaxies billions and billions of miles off are moving away? We can barely make them out, even with a powerful telescope.

The answer is the spectroscope, one of the most important instruments of sky science today. It is a combination of a prism and a viewing lens.

Hold a prism up to sunlight. It breaks the light into all the colors of the rainbow, ranging from violet on the left to red on the right side. Such a band of colors is called a spectrum, and it gives us a tremendous amount of information about the sun, a star, or a distant galaxy.

Each element, when heated until it glows, has its own special pattern, or spectrum. Calcium, for example, produces two very wide lines when its light is passed through a spectroscope. If we analyze the light of a distant star and come upon these two lines in its spectrum, we know at once that calcium is present.

The spectroscope identifies elements on the stars as easily as fingerprints identify people.

The spectroscope may even give us an idea of the temperature of a star. Suppose a star's spectrum shows that iron is present. Then we know that the temperature of that mass of glowing gases is at least high enough to melt iron.

But how does the spectroscope give away the movement of galaxies?

Have you ever listened to a train whistle? Did you notice that as the train came nearer, the pitch of the whistle went up? Then as the train moved away, the pitch went down.

The tendency of a tone to rise or fall depending on whether it is coming toward or going away from you is known as the Doppler effect—after Christian Doppler, the man who discovered it.

What interests us right now is that the Doppler effect works not only for sound but also for light—even the light coming from galaxies.

Imagine that we are examining through a spectroscope the light arriving from a distant star. Imagine, too, that this star is moving toward us. Its pattern does not fall into its usual place on the spectrum, but shifts over to the violet (or left) side.

Imagine now a star that is moving away from us. Its pattern shifts over to the right (or red) side of the spectrum.

It is just as though the star were signaling to tell us in which direction it is going.

Now let us examine the galaxies through the spectroscope. In all cases—except for the few nearby galaxies in our local group—their light has been shifting to the red end of the spectrum. The signal they are flashing to us over billions of empty miles is saying: *We are moving away from you!*

Now to the most astounding part of this tale about the expanding universe.

Not all galaxies show the same amount of shift toward the red. The more distant galaxies reveal a bigger shift than those that are closer. This means that the farther galaxies are traveling faster than the nearer. The outermost galaxies are traveling the fastest, some at speeds of over 40,000 miles per second.

Before you can wink an eye, they will have gone thousands of miles farther from us. Galaxies we still faintly see may one day be so far away that they will be out of sight.

What about the galaxies we cannot see because they are so far from us? If the rule holds that the farther away a galaxy the greater its speed, then such galaxies must be approaching the speed of light. And some—if this is possible—must be racing neck and neck with light, and ultimately traveling even faster than light. We could never see these galaxies even if we built a telescope a billion times as powerful as the one on top of Mount Palomar. Some sections of the universe must forever remain hidden to our gaze.

The universe, then, is getting bigger every day. It has been estimated that at its present rate of expansion it should double in size in the next two billion years. And there seems to be nothing that can stop its growth. It is swelling up like an overactive yeast cake.

Why should the universe be behaving in this peculiar manner? When did it start expanding? Is there a link between the origin of the universe and its expansion?

Any attempt to solve the mystery of how the universe began must also include an explanation of why it is getting bigger.

A BIRTH CERTIFICATE FOR THE UNIVERSE?

DATING OUR GALAXY

Before we try to solve the mystery of how the universe began, let's see if we can find out how old it is.

What is your guess: one million years? two million? a billion? five billion? one hundred billion? a billion billion? More than that?

In the seventeenth century, Bishop Ussher (a countryman of Sir Isaac Newton), after considerable though unscientific study, came up with a universe just under a modest 6,000 years old. Some of his friends had even worked out the details. "It all began," they said, "on October 26th, 4004 B.C., at nine o'clock in the morning!"

We know today that their figures must have been more than a little off. Man himself has been on this earth for almost one million years.

Unlike Bishop Ussher and his friends, we can't hope to come up with an exact date. What we will try for is a general idea of the universe's age.

Our plan is simple: We will attempt to establish a beginning date for the earth, the meteorites, the solar system, the sun, and our galaxy. Then we should be able to say that the universe is at least as old as they are.

We'll start with an easy question: How old are the oceans?

It is no secret that the oceans are salty and that they get their salt from the rivers that empty into them. Each year the oceans become a little saltier.

We know how much salt there is in the oceans. We also know how much salt is added to the oceans every year. We divide the total amount of salt in the oceans by the amount that is added every year, and we arrive at the number of years that salt has been carried down to the sea.

How many years does that come to? Just about three billion. The oceans then have been around for at least three billion years. We don't have to work very hard to realize that the earth, therefore, must be even older than that.

Let's get up on dry land and see what we can do about the age of the rocks.

We can discover their age by measuring the amount of uranium *and* lead they contain. Uranium is a radioactive element. In the course of time it decays and turns into lead. As the years go by, the amount of uranium decreases and the amount of lead increases.

We use the decay of uranium to check the age of the rocks, very much the way we use an old-fashioned egg timer to time an egg. Suppose it takes six minutes for all the salt in the upper part of the egg timer to flow into the lower, and we want a three-minute egg. Therefore, the moment the amount of salt at the bottom equals the amount at the top, we dash to the stove and rescue our egg. We determine the time by comparing the amount of salt left in the upper part of the glass with what has flowed into the lower part.

To determine the age of a rock, we compare the amount of lead that has been formed with the amount of uranium still remaining.

Our "uranium clock" tells us that the rocks of the earth are at least three and a half billion years old.

Now to see if we can use the moon as a "clock."

The moon is moving away from the earth. Not by much, just about five inches a year. But in a few billion years that adds up to quite a lot of mileage.

Let's imagine, as some astronomers do, that the moon originally was part of the earth, and let's go backwards in time. Every year we go back, the moon inches closer and closer to the earth.

How long will it be before the moon touches the earth? Four billion years!

We can assume that the moon left the company of the earth four billion years ago. The earth then must have been around for at least that long.

Have you noticed how each figure tends to confirm the previous one? If, according to our calculations, the oceans turned out to be six billion and the earth only two billion years old,

Northeast of San Diego, California, on 6,000-foot Mount Palomar, is the famous 200-inch Hale telescope. The "200-inch" refers to the diameter of the objective, or lens. A wide objective gathers more light than a small one, just as a lake catches more rainwater than a pond.

we'd know there was a joker someplace. But evidently we *are* on the right track.

We now examine a meteorite that has landed on our planet. We check its age with the uranium clock and find out that it is about four and a half billion years old.

Meteorites are probably fragments of a planet that never got started. Larger bits of it, the asteroids, are still circling the sun between Mars and Jupiter. The age of the meteorites indicates

35

that the other planets of the solar system were born at about the same time as our earth.

Let's question the stars. Stars, like women, are shy about their age. But with a little urging we can get them to admit their age—at least within a few billion years.

The age of our sun turns out to be five billion years, an estimate that fits in very neatly with what we know about the age of the earth and the other planets.

Are all the stars the same age? Not at all. Our sun is one of the young ones, hardly out of its knee pants.

The old-timers in our galaxy are the red giants. These graybeards—or shall we say red-beards—are eight billion years of age. Recently we discovered a few Milky Way stars that are really ancient: fifteen billion years old! We can safely conclude that our galaxy is at least that old, older by far than the earth, the planets, and the sun. If we were to issue a birth certificate for our section of the universe, under date of birth we'd write: 15,000,000,000 B.C.

Don't imagine that all astronomers agree on the exact time. But give or take a few billion years, they do agree that there was a time when our galaxy did not exist and that there came a time when it was born.

Perhaps you thought that our galaxy went back and back forever into the past. But it does seem that at one time there was no earth, no sun, no solar system, and no Milky Way. Then a grand event occurred: a birthday, and our glorious firmament of stars came into view.

Was the rest of the universe born at the same time? Does "fifteen billion" hold for all the galaxies? Is that the age of the universe?

Sorry, it's not that simple. Let's hold these questions until we have considered how the universe began.

We've done pretty well so far; we've dated a galaxy.

36

THE FIRST ATOMIC EXPLOSION

We are now ready to tackle the mystery of mysteries. How did the universe begin?

According to Georges Lemaître, the Belgian astronomer, the flying apart of the galaxies should furnish us with the key to the riddle. Something must have happened on the day the universe was born that causes it to expand. What could it be?

"Today we see the universe getting larger and larger," Lemaître said. "There must have been a time when it was much smaller. Suppose I had a motion-picture camera that has been taking pictures of the universe for billions of years.

"Viewing the film today, I see the galaxies fleeing from each other, each second getting farther and farther apart.

"Now, let me run the film backward. The galaxies reverse their direction and begin to move toward each other. The farther back I run my film, the closer the galaxies get. If I ran the film far enough, I'd see the galaxies crowd and jostle each other and the stars collide and dissolve in vast clouds of gas.

"The crush continues. The universe shrinks until all the material in the billions and billions of galaxies is crowded in an area no larger than the solar system.

"Matter becomes packed tighter than sardines in a can, tighter than the atoms on a black dwarf star, so tight that a teaspoonful weighs more than a 100 million tons.

"This is what it must have been like," continues Lemaître, "when our present universe was created. Matter was squeezed under unimaginable pressure, and something had to give way. The mass burst open and flew into space.

"We think we see the universe expanding. What we are actually seeing is an explosion that was touched off about seven billion years ago. The fireworks that announced the birth of the universe are still flying about in space."

How did the universe begin then?

"With a big bang," says Lemaître.

How does this theory strike you? Sounds as if it came right out of a science-fiction thriller, doesn't it? Yet many scientists give it serious consideration.

It helps to explain why the galaxies are running away. It also indicates how a universe held together by the grip of gravitation can still be flying apart. The force of the original explosion overcame even the enormous power of gravitation.

Notice, too, the resemblance to something we can see in the sky—a supernova. To create a supernova, matter is packed tighter and tighter within a very hot, shrinking star. Finally the star explodes and its material scatters into space.

Lemaître's creation is a souped-up, supercolossal supernova.

George Gamow, the American physicist, gives us some of the details of what may have happened on the day Lemaître's universe was born, eight billion years ago.

Just before the zero hour, all the atoms in the tight mass were squeezed into a pulp. They broke down and turned into what he calls "ylem," a mixture of neutrons and electrons. Matter ceased to exist. The universe was a concentrated package of energy, a kind of powerhouse that was all power and no machinery or building.

The intense pressure sent the temperature upward until it reached 25 billion degrees F. At this point, Gamow says, the "package" exploded and our universe came into being.

In less time than it takes to bake an apple pie, the temperature dipped to five million degrees F. In this "cool" atmosphere, matter was born.

Just as an atomic bomb explosion can produce new elements, this original blast created the hydrogen, oxygen, iron,

38

Universal matter con-
densed to a mass of
tremendous density.

This "power package"
(temperature: 25 billion
degrees F.) exploded.

Temperature dropped to
five million degrees F.
Elements formed.

Gravitation forced
gaseous matter to break
up into clouds.

Gas condensed, forming
stars within galactic
clouds.

Shrinking stars heated
up, releasing light and
heat. Planets formed.

silicon, gold, silver, and other elements that have endured for billions of years.

As the exploding gases spread out into space, their temperature continued to drop. Gravitation stubbornly struggled against the force of the explosion and finally managed to break the gases into separate clouds. Each cloud became a galaxy and continued its outward journey. Within each cloud the gases condensed and turned into stars.

Once in existence, the stars began to shrink. Growing smaller, they grew hotter. The rising temperature triggered off nuclear reactions. Hydrogen atoms fused and became helium. Vast stores of energy were released and became light and heat.

And it was at this point in the history of the universe that, one by one, the stars were turned on and heaven's light began to shine.

Not all of the original material of the galaxies was used up by the stars. Gamow believes that whatever was left over became the planets. The planets were very small and therefore cooled off rapidly. Unable to set up their own hydrogen power plant, they had to rely on nearby stars for their energy.

On one of the smaller planets of one of the smaller stars in one of the newly formed galaxies, a series of special events took place that turned out to be of some importance to us.

The light and heat coming from that small-sized star produced a number of odd physical changes on the surface of the planet. Green plants appeared, then animals that fed on the green plants. Finally, after billions of years on this tiny planet perched on the edge of the Milky Way, a two-legged, ten-toed, one-brained, warm-blooded creature appeared with an intelligence keen enough to ask: *How did the universe begin?*

A BIRTHDAY EVERY DAY

CREATION AT ALL HOURS

None of the two-legged, ten-toed, one-brained, warm-blooded creatures who live on this small planet is going to be satisfied that Lemaître and Gamow have taken him back to the *very* beginning of the universe.

How did that super-dense super-hot package of energy get there in the first place? What existed before the explosion?

Ask such questions of the astronomers who back this theory, and they say: "At the present time we don't know enough to answer your questions. We can only speculate. Perhaps the mass that exploded was the result of the shrinking of a previous universe, which in turn was the result of an earlier Big Bang.

"It is possible that the present expansion of space is already slowing down. The time may be coming when the galaxies will approach the earth, rather than fly from it. The universe will then contract and the process will start all over again.

"We may compare the universe to the heart of a cosmic giant, which grows larger, then contracts and then grows large again, each heartbeat taking about fifteen billion years."

These astronomers make us feel that we are gazing into a mirror in which we see ourself in a mirror seeing ourself in still another mirror, and so on.

They are not locating the beginning of the universe, but merely pushing the beginning farther and farther into the past. The trail they follow leads to a dead end!

But must the universe have a beginning?

Some astronomers think not.

According to the British scientist Fred Hoyle, we all have a strong feeling that things must have a start somewhere, sometime. We know that plants and animals and human beings are born. Even rivers and mountains and oceans have a beginning. Why not the universe?

"Scientifically, however," says Hoyle, "we have no grounds for such a feeling. I think it far more reasonable to say that the universe has always been here."

He suggests what he calls the "Steady-state" theory of creation. "Steady-state" means that the universe has not changed much in all of its existence. It is today just about what it was in the past.

Lemaître's theory, on the other hand, can be called an evolutionary theory, that is, the universe has changed, or evolved, ever since it was created.

Hoyle says, "Take a time-machine journey just as far back as you'd care to go—five billion years, fifty billion, a thousand billion—and you'll still find the universe around.

"Men, planets, stars, and galaxies are born, they grow old, and they die, but the universe remains. It was always here in the past, it will always be here in the future. It has always been and always will be much the same as it is now.

"The universe is eternal!"

Then the universe cannot have a birthday!

"Not at all," says Hoyle. "It does have a birthday. It has a birthday every day. It is this day, this hour, this moment. A little bit of the universe is being created all the time!"

How does Hoyle arrive at this strange idea? He starts, as do the other astronomers, with the expansion of the universe.

"The universe expands," he says, "and as it does space should be getting emptier and emptier because the distances between the galaxies are increasing all the time. In fact, with the galaxies rushing off so madly, you'd expect that after a few billion years or so we'd be left completely alone without another galaxy in sight.

"However, I don't think this will happen. If you and I should manage to come around even a hundred billion years from now, we'd still see *the same number* of galaxies in the sky. That is because for every galaxy that gives up its place in the universe, another comes to take its place."

Hoyle's universe is like a vast hotel with countless rooms. Each day guests depart on a journey to an unknown destination. But the manager is not troubled. He knows that for each guest that leaves, another will show up in his place. The guest list changes, but the hotel is always full.

Galaxies mysteriously vanish out of the universe, yet galaxies are always here.

All of this sounds like the act of a magician who can make rabbits appear and disappear at will. But rabbits, even magicians' rabbits, have to come from somewhere. Where are these brand-new galaxies to come from?

42

WAS THE UNIVERSE ALWAYS HERE?

Hoyle believes that the galaxies we see about us today—including our own—are growing old. As they grow old, they travel farther and farther apart. The universe does not empty out, however, because new galaxies appear to take the place of those that are gone.

But where are these new galaxies, with their billions of stars, to come from?

Hoyle says, "Aren't you forgetting Clue Number One, the presence of immense amounts of hydrogen in the spaces between the stars? This is the material out of which new galaxies are made."

We answer, "Yes, we know about this galaxy-forming gas out in space. We know what tremendous quantities of it there are. But won't the time come when it will all be gone, no matter how much you started with?"

"You're right," says Hoyle, "except that I believe the supply is constantly being renewed. Every moment newly created hydrogen is percolating into the universe to make up for the gas that is building fresh galaxies. You see, the universe does have a birthday every day. Every day a bit of the universe is born in the form of fresh hydrogen atoms."

Is this the reason that the universe is expanding?

"Exactly so," Hoyle says. "We don't need an explosion to explain why the universe is getting larger. It is the pressure of the newly created hydrogen that is forcing the universe to expand. Just as a balloon blows up to hold your breath, so the universe blows up to make room for newly formed hydrogen.

"New galaxies, new stars, and new planets are constantly being born. For billions of years they hold their place and then

43

Hydrogen is always being created throughout the universe.

Hydrogen collects in galactic clouds.

Clouds condense, spin, shrink, to form galaxies of stars and planets.

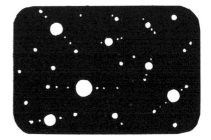

Within the stars, elements are created by nuclear reaction.

they disappear. In their place the universe gives birth to new hydrogen.

"The hydrogen collects in vast galactic clouds. The clouds break up into smaller clouds which condense and become stars. The stars spin and shrink. Their temperature shoots up, and a nuclear reaction begins. The hydrogen in the heart of the star cooks, its atoms fuse and become helium. The atomic cooking continues, and eventually all the other elements are formed in the furnace of the stars.

"And so the work of the universe goes on forever and forever."

Here they are then: the Evolutionary theory and the Steady-

44

state theory, the two principal ideas—at the present time—that attempt to tear away the curtain Nature has hung around the creation of her universe.

Can we accept the idea that everything started with a tremendous explosion? On the other hand, can we accept the idea that the material of the universe can be created out of nothing at all? Did the universe have a definite beginning or has it always been here? Did "creation" happen once or does it happen every day?

Now you see why we could not give a date for the beginning of things. We still do not have enough knowledge to say just how the universe happened.

Perhaps we'll have better luck when we get closer to home and investigate the beginning of the sun and the planets of our solar system.

THE SOLAR SYSTEM

On the preceding pages:
The sun during a total solar eclipse.

THE SOLAR SYSTEM

When we look up at a starry sky at night, it is hard to imagine that we really are part of the great galaxy of the Milky Way. It is just as hard to imagine that the earth we live on is part of a family of planets called the solar system.

The people of ancient times knew five of the planets: Mercury, Venus, Mars, Jupiter, and Saturn. But they thought they were stars. Hardly surprising. They certainly look like stars, don't they?

The ancient astronomers noticed that while most of the stars, such as the stars of the Great Dipper, seemed to be fixed in patterns, these five moved about the constellations in the course of the year. They therefore called them planets, or wanderers.

Only after the invention of the telescope, three hundred years ago, were men certain the planets are not stars at all.

To get a picture of what the solar system looks like, let's climb several billion miles into the heavens.

Directly below us is the sun with nine planets circling around it. They are all moving on the same level, as though on an invisible wheel with the sun at the hub.

Where is our earth? We are the third planet, counting out from the sun, one of the inner set of four small planets. The planets seem to be arranged in two groups: the inner group of small planets, Mercury, Venus, the earth, and Mars; and the outer group of four giants, Jupiter, Saturn, Uranus, and Neptune, plus the small, outermost, mysterious Pluto.

Notice that all the planets are traveling in the same direction around the sun—counterclockwise—and that they are all spinning in that direction. The sun, too, is spinning counterclockwise. One-way traffic is the rule in the solar system.

Like the Milky Way, the solar system is mostly empty space. Although there are only nine major planets and one star, they have spread themselves across eight billion miles of the heavens. Some of the planets keep a billion miles apart.

Imagine the sun the size of a small melon. Then the four inner planets (Mercury, Venus, earth and Mars) would be the size of pinheads, 20, 40, 60, and 80 feet from the sun. Jupiter, Saturn, Uranus, and Neptune would be the size of green peas, 250, 500, 1,000, and 1,500 feet away from the sun. Pluto would be a pinhead 2,000 feet away.

There is plenty of elbow room for everyone in the solar system.

How did the solar system begin?

Did the planets come together by chance? What holds them together? Why don't they go whirling off into space by themselves? Why are they moving and spinning in the same direction? Why are there two sets of planets?

We'd like to know the answers if only because we are part of the solar system. But we have an even better reason: The solar system contains life.

If we know how the solar system began, we may be ready for the most fascinating question of all: Is there life elsewhere in the universe?

Let's say that this family of the sun and its planets is just a freak, an accident. Then it probably is the one and only solar system in all of creation. Then life here is the only life in all of creation—and man is alone in all the vastness of the universe.

But suppose, just suppose, we could show that there is nothing so unusual about the way our solar system began, that solar systems are popping up all the time, that there are countless solar systems. Then we could say there is a good chance, an excellent chance, that life exists in other parts of the universe. Even more, that there are beings elsewhere as intelligent

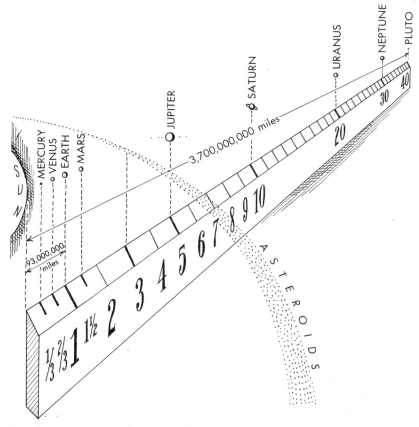

The planets are spaced out from the sun at fairly regular intervals. Mercury is about ⅓ the distance of the sun to the earth; Venus, ⅔; Mars, 1½ times the distance; the asteroids, 3 times; Jupiter, 5 times; Saturn, 10 times; Uranus, 20 times; Neptune, 30 times; and Pluto, 40 times. Can this be accidental?

51

as we are and just as much interested in getting at the answers!

Let's examine our solar system a little more carefully. We may come upon a number of important leads.

PLANET OF ENDLESS DAY AND ENDLESS NIGHT

MERCURY

Suppose we take a giant step of 36 million miles out from the sun. We land on Mercury, the first of the four inner planets.

The astronomers of ancient Greece noticed that it was the swiftest of the planets, circling around the sun in less than three months, and they therefore named it in honor of the winged messenger of the gods of Olympus.

A year on Mercury—the time it needs to travel once around the sun—is only three months long. On Mercury, therefore, you'd have four birthdays for every one you have on earth.

But a day on Mercury is endless. The planet spins so slowly that the same side always faces the sun, just as the same side of the moon always faces the earth. On the sun side of Mercury, it is always day; on the side away from the sun, it is always night.

Would you like to live sunny-side up or dark-side up on Mercury?

Don't answer! On the sun side the temperature goes up to 700 degrees F., hot enough to melt lead. On the night side the temperature is the lowest in the entire solar system, close to –459 degrees F., or absolute zero. Not even Pluto, three and a half billion miles from the sun, ever gets that cold.

Mercury is at one and the same time the hottest and the coldest planet in all the sun's family.

One reason for this peculiar condition is that Mercury is a planet without an atmosphere. A blanket of air, like a large

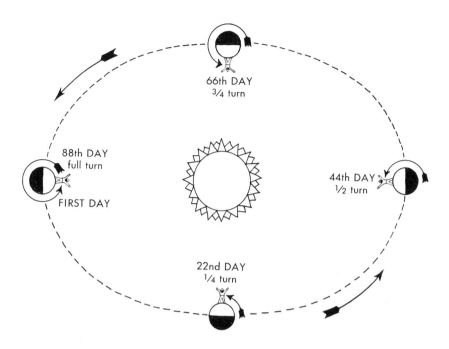

66th DAY
¾ turn

88th DAY
full turn

FIRST DAY

44th DAY
½ turn

22nd DAY
¼ turn

Mercury circles the sun in 88 days, the same time it takes to turn on its axis once. It spins so slowly that one side always faces the sun. On Mercury you could keep the sun in sight all year without shifting your position—that is, if you did not mind a temperature of 700 degrees F.

body of water, prevents extremes of heat and cold. On earth at night the air retains some of the heat that the sun has poured down during the day. Without an atmosphere we'd be unbearably cold after sundown.

Air is made up of gases like oxygen, water vapor, nitrogen, and carbon dioxide. Gases generally expand, and they keep on expanding until they escape into space. Fortunately, the earth has enough gravitational power to hold them captive.

But Mercury doesn't weigh much and is very small, only three thousand miles across; it could be dunked into the Atlantic Ocean without touching either the shore of Europe or North America. Therefore it has so little gravitational pull that on its surface a 100-pound "earth" boy would weigh only 25 pounds.

Whatever atmosphere Mercury ever had slipped out of its grasp a long time ago.

Because there is no air on Mercury to scatter the sun's rays, its sky is black. It is a planet without weather. Winds never blow and rain never falls. It is without sand or soil, for its rocks can never wear down.

Mercury is a burning wasteland on one side and a frozen tundra on the other. What are the chances of finding life on Mercury? None whatsoever.

THE MYSTERY PLANET

VENUS

Another giant step takes us from Mercury to Venus.

From the earth, Venus is a brilliant, all-white star low in the early evening or early morning sky. It outshines all the stars, and except for the sun and the moon it is the brightest and loveliest body in the heavens. Its light—reflected from the sun —is strong enough to cast a shadow after dark. It's not surprising that the Romans named it after the goddess of beauty.

If there is one planet in the solar system that is the earth's twin, it is Venus. In size and weight and materials, it is very much like our planet. It even contains the same amount of iron. You could walk and run and dance on Venus as you do on the earth, since the gravitational forces are about equal. If life has any chance away from our globe, it should be on Venus.

"Just let us penetrate the thick layers of yellow cloud that keep us from seeing the surface of this planet, and we'll find many signs of life," said some astronomers. "We'll come upon vast oceans, steaming jungles, an atmosphere containing oxygen, and intelligent Venusians."

These astronomers were aware that life depends on the

How did the moon get its "craters"? Possibly, three or four billion years ago, material from the dust cloud that helped form our solar system rained down on the moon and left these scars behind.

The nebulae (vast masses of glowing gas and dust) that we can see with telescopes are located in our own galaxy, the Milky Way. The Great Nebula in the constellation Orion *(right)*, only 1,000 light-years away, is about 600 trillion miles in diameter. Such nebulae are the birthplaces of stars.

The Dumbbell Nebula is about 3,400 light-years from the earth. It is expanding and, at the same time, probably rotating.

The eleven color photographs in this section (copyright 1959 and 1961, California Institute of Technology) were taken by William C. Miller at Palomar Observatory, using Super Anscochrome film, the 200-inch Hale telescope, and the 48-inch Schmidt telescope. Among the first color photographs ever taken of nebulae and galaxies, they are a milestone in the history of astronomical photography.

Below: Jupiter, king of the planets, contains more than twice the amount of matter of all the others together. The dark patch is the Great Red Spot, which suddenly appeared in 1878 and has been fading ever since. It is probably a disturbance deep within the planet's atmosphere.

Right: No, this is not the moon—it's the planet Venus, which goes through phases, from crescent to full, just as the moon does.

Bottom: The three rings of Saturn are formed of swarms of tiny satellites, each no larger than a grain of sand. The outermost ring is so faint, it can't be seen in this photograph.

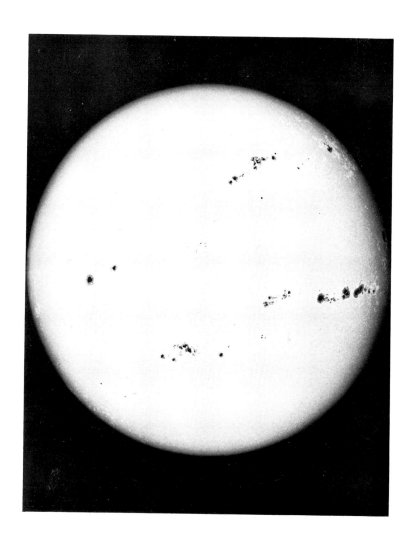

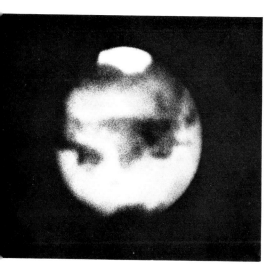

Above: The star nearest the earth is our own sun. If we came within 90 million miles of any other star as large and as radiant, it would look exactly like the sun to us. The dark blotches are sunspots.

Left: Through a telescope, Mars shows gray-green patches that might be lowly forms of vegetation. In this photograph we can make out one of the polar caps; these are possibly clouds of ice crystals or layers of frost.

Left: Pleiades, in the constellation Taurus, is an open cluster of about 760 stars, many of them invisible to us. Dust and gas show up as glowing clouds around the brightest stars.

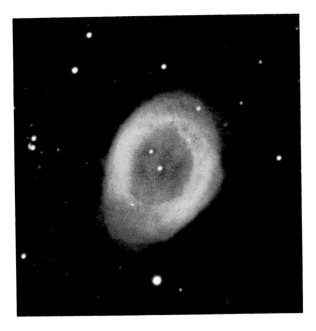

Left: The Ring Nebula, in the constellation Lyra, is an illuminated shell of gas surrounding an extremely hot central star.

Right: Here we are in the Milky Way, near the constellation of Cygnus, the Swan. This cloud is called, appropriately enough, the North American Nebula. With a little imagination, you can make out Mexico, Florida, the northern United States, and Canada.

Now we step out of the Milky Way into infinite space, and after hundreds of thousands of light-years we come to another galaxy with its own stars and planets, and perhaps life. M 81 is a spiral galaxy that resembles our own. The "M" refers to Messier's Catalogue.

Spiral galaxy NGC 4565 looks like a flying saucer only because we see it edge-on. If we could see it full face, it would probably look like M 81 *(right)*. The dark band along the edge is made up of dust clouds. Within our Milky Way, dust of this kind is seen, with the naked eye, as black patches.

Right: The Crab Nebula is the debris of a star that blew up in 1054; for some time after the explosion, it was so bright it could be seen during the day. Such an exploded star is called a supernova. Only two others have been noted within our galaxy: the first in 1572 by the great Danish astronomer Tycho Brahe, and the second by his pupil Johannes Kepler only thirty-two years later.

Right: The galaxies stretch on and on through infinite space. NGC 253 is a spiral galaxy, but its arms cannot be seen in this end-on view. "NGC" refers to the New General Catalogue, a modern listing of galaxies, nebulae, and other heavenly objects.

Above left: The Veil Nebula is a seething cloud of dust and gas located in the constellation Cygnus, the Swan.

Below left: The Lagoon Nebula is 2,600 light-years away from us. Within such a nebula, the density of hydrogen is many times greater than in average interstellar gas.

This spiral galaxy—M 51 in Canes Venatici—has a satellite galaxy trailing after it. The Magellanic Clouds are similar satellites of our own galaxy.

Above: M 31, a spiral galaxy framed by the constellation Androm-eda, looks very much like the Milky Way. It is about two million light-years away and contains more than 100 billion stars.

Below: M 104 in Virgo (seen edge-on) is, like M 51 and M 31, a spiral galaxy.

Left: Enmeshed within the gas and dust of the Rosette Nebula in the constellation Monoceros is an exceptionally bright star. It provides the energy that radiates out from the nebula.

Below: The curving arms of spiral galaxy M 33 give it the appearance of a pinwheel.

NGC 5128, a powerful emitter of radio waves, looks like a great storm in the skies. What is it? Probably a head-on collision of two galaxies. Gas and dust mingle, but the stars are so far apart that there is very little chance of any star collisions.

The twelve black-and-white photographs in this section were taken at Mount Wilson and Palomar Observatories.

speed at which a planet spins on its axis. If our spin, for example, slowed down, we'd sizzle on one side of the earth and freeze on the other. They were banking on the thought that, since Venus resembles the earth in so many ways, it ought to spin as the earth does.

But the best-laid plans of mice and stargazers often go astray. When the astronomers did finally penetrate the curtain of Venusian clouds, with spacecraft Mariner II, they found that the chances of life on the queen of planets are not very promising. In fact, they are quite bad.

The radio signals returned to the craft from the surface of the planet indicated that Venus turns around only once a year. One face is permanently fixed to the sun. The temperature on this side goes up to 600 degrees F., hot enough to boil eggs three times over, but a bit warm to encourage life. The temperature on the other side has yet to be determined.

The dense Venusian clouds are probably composed of dust and droplets of oil, and the oceans on Venus may turn out to be oceans of oil, not water. Venusian rain might bring smiles to the face of a gas-station owner, but wouldn't make a farmer happy.

Another disappointment: Venus's atmosphere is made, not of oxygen, but of carbon dioxide, the gas we breathe out as a waste product. Any oxygen Venus ever had probably combined with iron to form rust a long time ago.

Our oxygen here on earth would be lost in the same way were it not for the presence of plants and trees. Green plants absorb carbon dioxide, or CO_2. They use the carbon (C) for food and return the oxygen (O_2) to the air.

Conditions on Venus make it impossible for plants to live, and without them there can be no free oxygen. Without water or oxygen, Venus is doomed to be a lifeless planet forever.

But if there are little green men with antennas for ears who somehow or other have managed to keep going on Venus, they may be tuning in this weather forecast on their little green radios: *Weather unbearably hot. Not a breath of fresh air. Fallout of scalding oil expected today!*

A CHANCE FOR LIFE

MARS

Another giant step and we are on earth, where we stop just long enough for a glass of water and a breath of fresh air.

Again a huge step and we land on the red planet, Mars. We know more about Mars than any other planet except our own. Once every seventeen years it is only 35 million miles away from us. Watch for the next approach in 1971.

Although Mars is farther from us than Venus is, we see it more clearly because we can view it with the sun at our backs. Besides, heavy clouds don't curtain its surface. On occasion a few thin clouds scud westward across the Martian sky at 60 miles an hour. Strong winds must be blowing on Mars, just as on earth. And where there is wind, there must be air.

We can make out a much better case for life on Mars than we can for Venus. Mars spins at the same speed as the earth, its day and night are the same as ours, and it thereby avoids the extremes of heat and cold we find on Mercury and Venus.

Since the axis of Mars is tipped like the earth's, it too enjoys four seasons in the year. It does, however, take twice as long as the earth to make one complete circuit of the sun, so that each season in its "two-year" year lasts twice as long as ours do. (Your Martian age would be half your earthly years.) Like us, Mars has a moon or rather two moons, Phobos and Deimos, each about ten miles across.

Mars is much smaller and lighter than the earth. Its diameter is only one half ours, and it has only two fifths of our gravitational pull. If you can lift fifty pounds on earth, you'll have no difficulty showing off with 125-pound weights on Mars. Nevertheless, the planet has enough pull to hold on to an atmosphere of water vapor, carbon dioxide, and some oxygen. In the summer season, the temperature in the Martian tropics is quite bearable, ranging from about 60 degrees F. at noon down to below freezing at night.

Examine Mars through a telescope from season to season, and you'll be excited about the possibilities for life.

With the coming of winter, we can see a white area creeping over the polar regions, just as if snow or ice had fallen. Then as spring and summer advance, we see the polar caps grow smaller and smaller, as if the ice were melting away in the heat of the sun. At the same time we see the brown regions in the middle of the planet turn green.

Is it really ice or snow that we see in the white regions? But then why do they shrink so much in the spring?

On earth, even in the middle of the summer, our Arctic regions don't retreat; the ice is far too deep. Perhaps the Martian "arctic zones" are covered by a thin coat of snow or frost that is quickly melted by the spring sun.

Does the melted snow release water vapor which comes down as rain in the Martian tropics? Do plants come to life then and give the surface of Mars its green cast?

And if plants, why not animals; and if animals, why not intelligent beings who this moment are impatiently awaiting our first interplanetary visit?

Unfortunately for our high hopes, we won't be greeted by very intelligent beings when we do visit Mars. At the very best, we will find only lowly mosses and lichens, the kind that grow on barren rocks above the Arctic Circle. Mars has so little oxygen that we'd be fooling ourselves if we expected to encounter higher forms of life.

Look up at Mars, even without a telescope, and you'll see why. Its red appearance, which led to its being named for the Roman god of war, is caused by iron rust. Most of the surface of Mars is composed of rusted iron. A long time ago, the iron in the rocks of Mars absorbed most of the oxygen in the atmosphere. So, when you visit Mars, don't forget to pack a liberal supply of oxygen. The air is thinner than that at the top of Mount Everest.

Mars, then, is really not very friendly to life. Most of the planet is a freezing desert like the most exposed parts of Tibet.

We start out with high expectations and end up with a few scraggly mosses and lichens. But it is exciting to know that some form of life, lowly as it is, might exist on another planet.

Life is impossible on Mercury and Venus. It is struggling for a foothold on Mars. Beyond Mars, the planets offer no hope of life at all.

But between Venus on one side and Mars on the other, there is a planet where life *does* flourish, our own earth. Are we located in a kind of "life zone"? If our planet had been placed nearer the sun or farther away, life might never have come into existence here.

A question comes to mind. Far out in space, beyond our solar system, are there other planets circling about other stars? Are some of these planets located in a life zone? What are the chances of finding life similar to ours on such planets?

But let's hold these questions off until we have had a chance to consider how the solar system began.

58

THE ASTEROIDS

If you are going to take your usual giant step out from Mars, watch out! You will not land on another planet. The planetary tracks are regularly spaced out from the sun. But on the track beyond Mars, no planet runs.

The organization of the planets seems to break down between Mars and Jupiter. Three hundred and fifty million miles of empty space between the two, and not a planet in sight.

"Perhaps we are just overlooking a planet," said the astronomers at the end of the eighteenth century.

Eagerly they scanned this section of the heavens almost foot by foot. And they found not one, but thousands of heavenly bodies!

On the track where the missing planet should have been running are countless bits of planetary matter. Here the sky is peppered with what we now call planetoids or asteroids, all merrily circling about the sun counterclockwise, like the planets. No more than a dozen of these asteroids are over a hundred miles in diameter. Most of them are just flying mountains, clumsily tumbling through the sky.

The biggest, Ceres, is only 480 miles across with a gravitational pull one-thirtieth that of the earth. Race a bicycle on some of the smaller asteroids, and you will find yourself launched into space.

Did I say that all of them circle the sun? Well, a few have grown tired of wheeling about on the same old planetary track year after year and have gone off to visit other parts of the solar system. One of them, Hermes, once almost dropped in on us, shaving the earth by only half a million miles.

No need to worry about colliding, though. There is a traffic rule of the sky known as the Roche Limit. It states that when a smaller body approaches within two and one-half times the radius of a larger body, the smaller will be shattered to bits. Thus any good-sized asteroid which ventured within ten thousand miles of us would explode before it got close enough to do any damage.

After 1,600 planetoids had been identified, astronomers ran out of names like Ceres, Hermes, Adonis, and those of other Greek gods. Some of the planetoids have since been named for the wives of astronomers, others for their pet dogs and cats, and still others for their favorite desserts.

How did these chunks of metal and rock get into the sky?

Since they are flying a planetary track, we'd like to think they are the flotsam and jetsam of a planet that foundered and broke up a long time ago.

Only thing wrong with the theory is that if you put all the pieces into a neat pile, they don't make up a mass as large as the moon.

Is it possible that when the material for the planets was gathered together, some of it was left over—but not enough to make up a healthy-sized planet? The asteroids may be the parts of a planet that never jelled.

SNOWBALL IN THE SKY

JUPITER

Almost 500 million miles from the sun, the giant Jupiter circles about the sky.

Mars is one and a half times, the asteroids are three times, and Jupiter is five times the distance of the earth to the sun. Although so far away, it is, with the exception of Venus, the brightest planet in the sky.

60

Named for the king of the Roman gods, it is the largest of all the planets, big enough to house all the others at the same time. Its gravitational pull is far greater than the earth's. If you tip the scales at 100 pounds on earth, expect to weigh 250 pounds if you get to Jupiter. Your puny earth-muscles could not lift you to a sitting position or help you draw a deep breath. A native of Jupiter would have to be enormously broad and short, like a Japanese wrestler.

Jupiter takes its time getting around the sun. Its "year" is as long as twelve of ours, but it more than makes up for its slow pace around the sun by the briskness of its spin.

A whirling dervish of a planet, Jupiter makes one complete turn every ten hours. It spins far faster than any of the inner planets. At its equator, Jupiter is traveling at 27,000 miles an hour. Compare that with our speed of 1,000 miles an hour.

Any heavenly body that turns around as fast as Jupiter must expect to bulge in the middle. Jupiter looks like a soft ball that has been pinched in, top and bottom. Even the earth, which is spinning so much more slowly, looks more like a grapefruit than a perfect sphere. Mercury and Venus, on the other hand, with practically no spin, are almost perfectly round.

Planets, unlike people, develop a bulge around their middle after too much activity, not too little.

Jupiter's spin is remarkable not only for its speed, but also for the fact that the whole planet is not spinning at the same rate. Different latitudes rotate at different speeds.

Every part of the earth takes the same length of time to rotate once. But on Jupiter, it all depends on where you are. It's as though New Orleans took less time than Chicago. Pity the poor calendar maker on Jupiter. What is Monday in one place is Wednesday or Friday somewhere else. Only something loose, like a liquid or a gas, can behave in such a way. Jupiter is not a solid.

61

Its outer layer is a mixture of frozen ammonia (cleaning fluid), methane (marsh gas), and hydrogen. Dive down through this poisonous stew for 10,000 miles and you'll hit, not land, but an iceberg with a temperature of –200 degrees F. Dig into this popsicle, and you will at last come upon a small core of rock and metal. The majestic king of the sky is nothing more than a slushy snowball with a hard center.

Don't be fooled by its size; Jupiter is a featherweight that could almost float in salt water. If it were made of the heavy substances that make up our earth, it would weigh at least four times as much.

But Jupiter still has enough sheer mass to give it enormous gravitational power. Surrounded by a family of twelve moons, it is able to hold on to four which are 15 million miles off. No other planet can boast of keeping in orbit satellites so far away.

Most of Jupiter's satellites, like most of the other moons of the solar system, circle counterclockwise. But the 15-million-milers of Jupiter travel just the other way.

Is it possible that these wrong-way moons were not always part of Jupiter's family? Could they be asteroids that were once yanked from their own track by Jupiter's gravitational lasso?

The discovery of Jupiter's moons in 1610 is one of the great moments in the history of science. Up to this time, men did not know of the existence of the solar system. They thought that the earth was the center of the universe, and that the planets and even the sun circled around the earth.

Then the great astronomer Galileo turned his newly invented telescope on the skies. One of his first discoveries was the moons of Jupiter.

"Look for yourselves, gentlemen," he cried out to his fellow professors at the University of Padua in Italy. "Notice that the moons of Jupiter are going around Jupiter; they are *not* going around the earth. Heavenly bodies need not circle the earth. If Jupiter can have satellites of its own, then surely the sun can. I believe that the planets are satellites of the sun and go around the sun. But come and see the moons of Jupiter for yourselves."

But the professors refused to see for themselves. It was wicked to believe that the earth was not the center of the universe, and they were not going to allow the facts to change their mind.

Not until the time of Newton were men ready to recognize the existence of the solar system.

RING AROUND A PLANET

SATURN

Nine hundred million miles out in space—ten times the distance of the earth to the sun—the planet Saturn slowly moves through the sky.

Among the six brightest objects we see from the earth, it was the most distant planet known to the ancient Romans. They called it Saturn, after the god of time, because of its slow twenty-five-year journey around the sun.

Like Jupiter, Saturn spins about on its axis once every ten hours, and again like Jupiter it has a bulge around its middle. It is the most flattened out of all the planets—it looks like a rubber ball some heavyweight has pressed under his big foot.

The second largest of the planets, Saturn is seven hundred times bigger than the earth. Yet it is only one hundred times heavier. The materials of which Saturn is made are so light that the planet could float in a tub of water if we could find one large enough.

If you were ever to set foot on Saturn, you'd sink into a cloud (at −243 degrees F.) of ammonia, methane, and hydrogen. Not surprising that Saturn can float. It is almost all foam.

Saturn also resembles Jupiter in having its own family of moons, nine of them, the outermost going the wrong way. Again we wonder if the straggler is a captured asteroid.

Saturn differs from Jupiter in one way that makes it the strangest object in the entire solar system.

Imagine a planet with a ring around it. You'd think you were dreaming or that the astronomers were playing a little joke. And yet all you have to do is to look up at Saturn through a telescope, and there it is—a ring, or rather three rings, circling around the planet.

Galileo, although he discovered the rings of Saturn, never knew what to make of them. Through his first crude spyglass, it looked as though a planet and two motionless moons were joined together in one strange, bulging mass.

Each of the rings is 40,000 miles wide and only ten miles deep. They look solid, although we can see the stars shining through them, and we know that different parts circle about Saturn at different speeds. Examine their light through a spectroscope, and you'll discover that the inner sections make more trips around the planet than the outer sections do. Certainly the rings are not all of one piece.

What are they?

A swarm of tiny particles, each about the size of a fine grain of sand. They are tiny moons, probably made of ice and as hard as stone, flying about so fast that they cannot be sucked into the planet.

How did this strange triple ring ever come into existence?

We can only guess. It's tempting to think that once upon a time one of the planet's moons carelessly wandered within the Roche Limit and instantly broke into a billion fragments, thereby giving the solar system its most spectacular show—the rings of Saturn.

URANUS, NEPTUNE, AND PLUTO

In the far outfield of the solar system, where the temperature, night and day, never goes above –300 degrees F., and where the sun is only a star in a forever darkened sky, the three most distant planets float: Uranus, Neptune, and Pluto.

Uranus is about twenty times farther from the sun than the earth is, Neptune about thirty times, and Pluto about forty times. Uranus is almost two billion miles away from us, and Neptune another billion miles beyond.

Despite their great distance, the sun keeps a firm gravitational grip on them. Uranus circles the sun in eighty-four years, and Neptune does it in just about twice that time. Since its discovery in 1846, Neptune hasn't had a chance to make one complete trip around the sun.

Uranus and Neptune are practically twins, both about the same size and both spinning around at a mad pace. Both show the usual rotational bulge that comes from too much planetary exercise. Both are iceboxes packed with methane and ammonia. Unlike Jupiter and Saturn, they seem to have very little hydrogen.

In one respect, Uranus differs from Neptune—indeed, from all the planets. All the others rotate from west to east, that is, counterclockwise. But Uranus spins at right angles to the rotation of the other planets because it is tilted way over on its side, like a top that has fallen over. If our earth were askew like Uranus, all our land and water masses would be reversed. The United States would be in the Southern Hemisphere, Florida would be on the West Coast, and California in the East. It's just as well that we continue right side up.

Almost a billion miles from Neptune is Pluto, the least

known of all the planets. Named for the Roman god of the underworld, Pluto steals about the outer fringes of the solar system, taking a remarkable total of 248 of our earth years to make one complete orbit of the sun.

Since it is way out in the solar outfield, you'd expect Pluto to be a giant among giants. On the contrary, it is a peewee of a planet only 3,600 miles across. Its size would seem to put it in the infield along with Mercury and Mars.

Unlike the giants that are mostly froth, Pluto is probably packed with solid materials just as the earth is. Then again, while the giants spin about in ten to sixteen hours, Pluto probably takes six days. Because of its great distance from the earth, we really know very little about it. But everything we do know about Pluto indicates that it doesn't belong in the neighborhood of Jupiter, Saturn, Uranus, and Neptune. And yet there it is, even further from the sun than they are.

How to account for Pluto?

It's about the same size as Triton, one of Neptune's moons. Could it possibly be that Pluto was once a satellite of Neptune? Then, breaking loose, it ran off by itself, only to be snatched up by the ever-alert and all-powerful sun and forced into a solar orbit?

Perhaps Pluto once belonged to another star. One day it escaped and started wandering through the heavens, then came too close to our sun and was promptly snared.

At the present time, we have no explanation that really fits the strange case of the god of the underworld.

What lies beyond Pluto? Is Pluto definitely the last planet of our sun system? Suppose we took other giant steps, fifty, sixty, seventy, eighty times the distance of earth to sun. Would we encounter planets that reflect so little sunlight that they cannot be seen, even by the most powerful telescopes?

The solar system may be vastly larger than the one visible to us today.

COMETS AND METEORS

Besides the planets and their satellites and the asteroids, there are several junior members of the sun's family: the comets, the meteors, and the meteorites.

The planets and the moons are steady, domesticated creatures. But the comets, meteors, and meteorites are the untamed wildstock of the solar system. We often can't tell what they are up to or where they are going. They change their shape and size and often disappear altogether.

A comet—sometimes called a hairy star—is a body of glowing gases that flies an orbit around the sun. The orbit may extend billions of miles out into space beyond the farthest planet, but the comet somehow or other finds its way back to the sun even after many years.

Far out in space, a comet might move no faster than a trot-

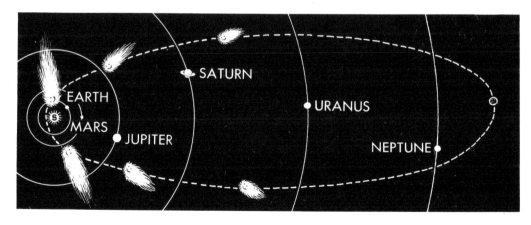

The orbit of Halley's Comet about the sun. The pressure of sunlight forces small particles to flow from the head of a comet into its tail, which therefore points away from the sun. We generally think of a tail as trailing behind, but a comet moving away from the sun is *preceded* by its tail!

ting horse. As it begins to home in on the sun, it travels faster and faster, reaching speeds up to a million miles an hour.

The head swells larger and larger, and at the same time a tail appears which grows longer as the comet gets closer to the sun. A halo envelops the head; the tail glows and spreads across the heavens.

No wonder men once thought the end of the world was at hand when a comet appeared. When the comet of 1456 flashed in the heavens, prayers were read in all the churches of Europe: *Protect us, O Lord, from Satan, the Turk, and the Comet.*

Even in the twentieth century, men could still be frightened. In 1910, when Halley's Comet was due, people were certain they were about to be wiped out by poisonous gases. But the earth passed right through the tail of the comet, and no one was any the worse for it.

Comets look terrifying but they are as harmless as the Northern Lights or a rainbow. A comet tail millions of miles long is astonishingly thin—it holds less than one ounce of material. It is finer than the vacuum in a television tube. The head is so flimsy that the stars can be seen through it. Occasionally, the head is fitted with an "eye" made up of tiny pebbles and bits of ice.

The total weight of the twenty billion or so comets that circle the sun is less than that of the earth. Comets are the ghosts of the solar system.

Urged on by the gravitational pull of the sun, the comet races in, its tail dragging behind like the vapor trail of a jet. But once it passes around the sun, something unexpected happens: The tail is now in the lead with the head following!

Why such odd behavior?

The gases that make up 99.9 percent of a comet are so weak that sunlight exerts pressure on them. You've seen dead leaves scattered by a stream of water. So are the gases within a comet hurled back by a stream of sunbeams.

During the last visit of Halley's Comet, in 1910, the head glowed like the brightest stars, and at one point the 37-million-mile tail stretched 120 degrees across the sky. The comet should be on its way back to us now, and you can expect a similar show in 1985.

Mount Wilson and Palomar Observatories

Once a comet is far enough away from the sun, its tail grows smaller and smaller and finally disappears. All head again, the comet departs for outer space. Hundreds, perhaps thousands of years later, the same comet returns to repeat its acrobatic stunts.

How did comets begin?

Odd as their conduct is, they are certainly children of the solar system. No matter how far they fly, they always return to the sun.

They are made up chiefly of nitrogen, CN (cyanogen), ammonia, carbon monoxide, and ice, materials you'd expect to find on one of the four giant planets. Perhaps the comets are formed of what was left over when these giants were born.

We may not be too certain of how comets are born, but we have a pretty good idea of how they die.

In 1846 Biela's Comet put on a wonderful show. Right before the eyes of the entire world, it broke in two. On its return five years later, it showed up as two comets a million miles apart. Five years later it did not show up: in its place came a shower of meteors, or shooting stars. Biela's Comet never appeared again. When a comet dies it becomes a swarm of meteors.

You can easily see meteors when the earth passes through a great shower of them, such as the Perseids in early August.

Meteors rain down on the earth night and day, although we cannot see them during daylight hours. The whole earth collects a truckload of five to ten billion every twenty-four hours. It would not have to be a very big truck since each meteor is only the size of a pinhead.

At what point in their descent do we see meteors? When they are about sixty miles from the earth. Traveling at a great speed, they strike the air with tremendous force, catch fire, and are snuffed out before they ever reach the ground.

A famous comet, which is not yet ready to become a shower

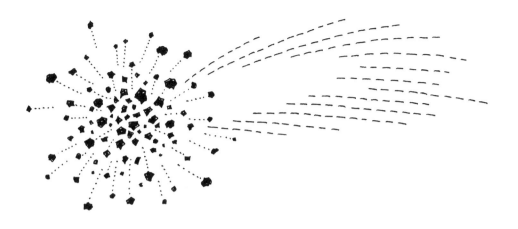

When a comet breaks up, it becomes a stream of meteors, or shooting stars.

of shooting stars, is Halley's Comet, named after the English scientist Edmund Halley, a friend of Newton.

This comet was first noticed 240 years before Christ, but in those days no one thought that a comet could come back at regular intervals.

Halley, after looking over the old records, was amazed to find that the comets that appeared in 1531, in 1607, and in 1682 were very much alike.

"Is it possible," he thought, "that we've been looking at the same comet without knowing it? I'd like to predict that we'll find this comet back with us in 1759."

Unfortunately for Halley, he never lived to see the triumph of his prophecy. But his comet did return in 1759. And then in 1835 and then again in 1910.

When can we expect it next?

A little subtraction will tell you that it is running on a schedule of approximately seventy-five years. The next time should be 1985. But if by any chance Halley's Comet fails to show up and there is a shower of meteors instead, you'll understand.

Don't blame it on your arithmetic.

METEORITES

Shooting stars rarely reach the earth's surface, but other visitors from outer space do.

Meteorites are chunks of material that dive to the earth from out of the sky. Some weigh up to thirty tons. Unlike shooting stars, they are so large and so cold that they do not burn up on striking the atmosphere, but keep right on going until they hit the earth.

In Arizona, not too far from the Petrified Forest, there is a huge hole in the ground that looks like a mile-wide crater on the moon. Several thousand years ago, a meteorite, traveling at ten times the speed of a rifle bullet, crashed into the solid rock and gouged out a hole 500 feet deep. Bits of the meteorite can still be found today, scattered more than six miles away from the crater.

Meteorites reach the earth every day, but most of them are never noticed. Two thirds fall into the ocean, and many bury themselves deep within the ground. Those on the ground eventually rust and break up.

Like shooting stars, meteorites glow as they plunge through the air, but it is only the surface that is heated. Millions of years of exposure to the cold of outer space have given meteorites a temperature close to absolute zero. A few minutes of whizzing through our atmosphere removes only a little of the chill.

You can touch a meteorite soon after it lands without getting burned. One that fell in a steaming jungle became enveloped in ice shortly after hitting the earth.

The tremendous difference between the temperature of the

72

A legend of the Hopi Indians says that Barringer Crater in Arizona—¾ of a mile across and 600 feet deep—marks the spot where a god descended from heaven in fiery majesty. Actually, it is a scar made by the impact of a giant nickel-iron meteorite that struck the earth about 2,500 years ago.

atmosphere and the extreme cold within a meteorite may cause it to explode. In 1908, a huge meteorite fell in Siberia and burst. Trees were blown over, a herd of reindeer was wiped out, and a pressure wave was recorded in England, over 3,000 miles away.

Run your hand over a meteorite. What mysterious substances from outer space are you touching?

None! Only materials we have here at home: stone, nickel, iron, and other common metals.

The message meteorites bring us is that the substances of the

73

sky are the same as the substances of the earth. Meteorites confirm what the spectroscope has already told us: Nature uses the same familiar materials throughout her universe.

Where do meteorites come from?

Let's examine a specimen in the laboratory. There are two kinds of meteorites: those made of stone and those made of metal. Place a bit of an iron-nickel meteorite under the microscope. Notice that the metal looks as though it had hardened after having once been in a liquid state.

Now where in the solar system would we expect to find iron or nickel in liquid form?

Only in the heart of a planet. The core of the earth, for example, is a lake of liquid iron.

How could metal deep inside a planet get outside? Probably by means of a tremendous blast that must have torn the poor planet apart. We are back to the theory of a lost planet, a planet that blew up and scattered its metal and stone crumbs all over the solar system. Are meteorites, then, part of the debris left over by that explosion?

By careful analysis of a meteorite, we can even estimate when the big blowup occurred: just about 300 million years ago when Tyrannosaurus Rex, the king of dinosaurs, stalked the earth. Neither he nor his relatives are left to tell us what happened.

What kind of planet must it have been? Certainly not like the four outer giants which are all froth and gas. It must have been a hard stone-and-metal planet, like Mercury, Venus, Mars, and the earth.

And so the meteorites leave us with a persistent question: Not so many hundreds of millions of years ago, was there really a neighboring planet in the sky that one fine day came to a sudden and spectacular end?

74

THE NEBULAR HYPOTHESIS

How orderly and well regulated the solar system is!

It is like a railroad in which all the trains run on time, taking the passengers to their destinations with never a delay or accident. What brought all the planets together and set them going on their timetables? How did the solar system begin?

Philosophers, mathematicians, scientists, and just ordinary people have fought and argued over the riddle for a long time, each insisting he was right and the other fellow wrong.

But not one of them was around when the system began. All that anyone can offer is a theory, or, as we say, an informed guess.

How can we tell whether one man's theory is better than another's?

By asking each theory to give satisfactory answers to four test questions:

> Why do the planets travel around the sun?
> Why are the planets moving in the same direction?
> Why are the four small inner planets made of heavy materials and why are the four outer giants made of light materials?
> How could the slow-spinning sun have been the parent of planets that whirl about so swiftly?

The first man in modern times to dare a "scientific" explanation of how the solar system began was the French mathematician Pierre Simon de Laplace. At the beginning of the nineteenth century, he suggested a theory called the nebular hypothesis.

Before the solar system existed, said Laplace, there was a vast cloud of gas, or a nebula, in the heavens.

This nebula stretched out at least as far as the present boundaries of the solar system, but gravitation gradually pulled it inward. As it grew smaller, it began to spin.

Now we know from our study of the four outer giants that a fast-spinning body flattens out on top and bottom and builds a bulge around the middle.

The shrinking nebula, whirling faster and faster, became the sun. The bulge grew bigger and bigger. Finally it could no longer hold on, and off it went into space, the way mud is cast off your bicycle wheel. The castoff material became the planets, and they have continued their circular motion around the sun to this very day.

A very nice theory, you'll admit! How neatly it accounts for the fact that all the planets are traveling around the sun, and all in the same direction.

Unfortunately, it is full of holes. The sun is over 99 percent hydrogen and helium, and yet it is supposed to have given birth to planets like the earth, which are mostly stone and iron.

But the real trouble is that the theory doesn't even try to explain the sun's spin. Here is the sun, lazily turning on its axis once every twenty-seven days. And here are the giant planets whirling about at dizzying speeds. How could a slowpoke sun have been the parent of such active children? How could the planets have gotten so much go-round from a sun that hardly stirs itself?

It's as though you were idly swinging a rock around over your head, and then, when you let go, it suddenly began to whir about you at a dizzying speed. A sun powerful enough to throw off the planets and keep them moving should be spinning fifty times as fast as ours actually is.

76

In the light of what we know today about the movement of the sun and the planets, the nebular hypothesis just does not hold up.

COLLISIONS AND EXPLOSIONS

Scientists were disappointed that the nebular hypothesis failed to explain the make-up of the planets and the difference in the go-round of the sun and its family. But they could not entirely give up the idea that the sun and the planets started life together.

In our own century astronomers—such as T. C. Chamberlin and Moulton in the United States and Sir James Jeans in England—have dreamed up traffic accidents in the skies to get the solar system going.

"Let us imagine," they say, "that once upon a time another star dared to move in on our territory in the Milky Way. The stranger and the sun, irresistibly drawn to each other by mutual gravitation, came closer and closer. At the last moment, just before the fatal crash that would have snuffed out both of them, the stranger veered aside and went his way.

"But just as the moon raises tides on the oceans of the earth, so the invading star raised a huge tide of gases on the face of the sun. Yanked from the sun, the material streamed into space and became the planets. The gravitational pull of the passing star gave them the momentum to circle and whirl about as rapidly as they do."

Let's give this theory an A for effort—but for nothing else. What's wrong is that the other stars are so far away from us

77

that it is almost impossible that one of them ever came that close. The stars know how to keep their distance.

But let us suppose that a star did once come close enough to wrench huge gobs of gas from the sun. This gas would be so hot—about ten million degrees F.—that it would explode with tremendous force and vanish completely from the solar system.

Astronomers like their science fiction, just as you and I, and next they came up with a real thriller.

This theory is based on the fact that almost half the stars in heaven are double, or binary, stars. Binaries are pairs of stars that move around one another for company. Look up at the sky on a bright night and the chances are that a good number of the stars you see are really two stars that look like one.

Sirius, the Dog Star, brightest in the heavens, is accompanied by a little star called (as you would expect) the Pup. Proxima Centauri, the star nearest us, chases around after one called Alpha Centauri.

Notice the star at the bend of the Big Dipper. If you have a sharp pair of eyes, you will notice another star, its partner, directly above it. A telescope will show you thousands of other binaries in the sky.

"Now," said the astronomers who thought up this new theory, "there's our sun all by itself. Don't you think it's curious that it doesn't have a companion? Let us imagine therefore that our sun at one time came equipped with a partner.

"Let us further imagine that this companion blew up, scattering its fragments all over the skies. But before they could get away, the sun snagged them with its gravitational lasso and has kept them in tow ever since. So the solar system came into existence."

One advantage of this guess is that it offers an explanation of why the earth and the other inner planets are made of stone and iron, materials that are so rare on the sun. We aren't the children of the sun after all. We are rather the children of a now-lost star that had plenty of such materials. The sun is only our foster parent.

Again, a neat theory! But there is a principle of science called "Occam's Razor," which says: "You don't need a far-fetched explanation when a simple one will do. Why go miles out of your way for an answer when it might be waiting for you right at your front door?"

Scientists today seek the origin of the solar system, not in a one-in-a-million accident, but in the natural growth and development of the universe.

OUT OF A CLOUD OF DUST

BIRTH OF THE SUN AND PLANETS

Nowadays astronomers, instead of dreaming up near-collisions, explosions, and other assorted nightmares, are more matter-of-fact about the birth of the solar system.

"Nothing so unique about our solar system," they say. "If a planetary family gathered around our star, then other planetary families have gathered around other stars. A planetary system is probably being formed this very moment in some distant corner of the universe."

Where is the material to come from that will build these solar systems?

"From the dust and hydrogen gas that lie between the stars."

But how can planets and suns be constructed of such material? Isn't it very thin?

"You're right, so thin that a matchbox full of it holds only a few atoms, as compared with the billions and billions of atoms we'd find in what we call an 'empty' matchbox here on earth. But as you know, space is so vast that the total amount of this material may outweigh that of all the stars in all the galaxies in the universe. Sometimes, for reasons we don't yet understand, this interstellar (meaning 'between-the-stars') gas and dust tend to gather together in clouds."

Can we see these clouds?

"You surely can. In the wintertime look at the constellation of Orion, the Mighty Hunter, through field glasses or a telescope. Below Orion's belt hang three dim stars, his sword. The hazy patch around the middle star is a dust cloud called the nebula in Orion. Planetary systems get their start in nebulas like these, and there may be thousands in our galaxy alone."

But how can a hazy patch in the sky become a sun and a family of planets like ours?

"Our sun and its family began as a dust cloud that extended over ten million billion miles of space. The cloud shrank and began to spin. The gas in the center became more and more concentrated and formed the sun, the outer part of the cloud turning like a great wheel around it.

"Just as an ice skater spins faster and faster when she brings her arms to her chest, so the wheel turned faster as it grew smaller.

"Now imagine a swiftly moving brook. As the water comes to a turn in the stream, it breaks into eddies that whirl about by themselves. In the same way, the turning cloud broke into vast whirlpools of gas and dust. These condensed into huge blobs which continued to grow smaller and heavier. The blobs collided, and the smaller ones clumped together to form the planets.

"The first planets were Jupiter, Saturn, Uranus, and Neptune, and their birth took place on the rim of the wheel. The smaller planets, Mercury, Venus, the earth, and Mars were born later on the inside of the wheel, much closer to the sun.

"In the beginning the sun was dark and much larger than it is today. But as it shrank, its temperature rose. The hydrogen atoms fused and turned into helium. Finally the sun began to shine in all its glory and send out its warming rays to all its newborn planets.

"In this way, according to our present theory, the solar system began."

QUICK PLANETS AND LAZY SUN

THE CRUCIAL TEST

We still have a few questions to ask about the Dust-cloud theory. Why should there be such a great difference between the outer and the inner planets?

"The giant planets," say the astronomers, "were formed first on the outer edge of the dust cloud, where the temperature was low enough for the gases to jell. These planets are bigger because they were able to snatch up most of the cloud material for themselves, especially the ammonia, methane, hydrogen, and water.

"When the region nearer the center cooled off, the inner planets could be built. Since very little lightweight material remained, these planets had to be content with the small amount of stone and iron left over from the original dust cloud. The outer planets, therefore, are gigantic and light—with the exception of Pluto. The inner planets are tiny and heavy."

But haven't we lots of water on the earth, an inner planet? Just look at all our oceans.

"Compared with Jupiter, Saturn, Uranus, or Neptune, we have very little water. Our water lies only on the surface and the vast bulk of the earth contains very little. The giants hold most of the water in the solar system in the form of ice."

Can the Dust-cloud theory explain the slow movement of the sun and the dizzying pace of the planets?

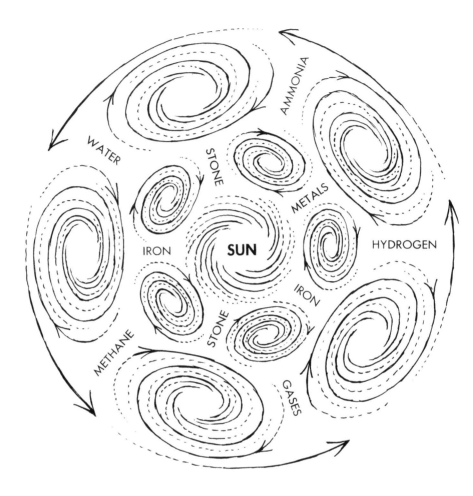

According to the Dust-cloud theory, the solar system began as a swirling cloud of nebular material. Spinning around, it flattened out like a phonograph record, and then broke up into blobs of gas and dust that cooled off and became the planets. Light materials, such as water, ammonia, hydrogen, and methane, were sorted out of the original cloud and formed the outer giant planets. The materials left over, such as stone, iron, and other metals, formed the inner and heavier planets, including the earth.

"Yes. We believe that the sun has not always turned at its present slow rate—almost a full month for one complete turn on its axis. When the solar system was new, the sun was spinning very rapidly—as fast as Jupiter is turning today.

"But in order to get the planets moving, the sun had to give them a push by yielding a good part of its angular momentum, or go-round. Like a proud parent who makes sacrifices for her children, the sun surrendered part of its spin so that the planets could show off their speed millions of miles away from home. Today the planets are moving with exactly the momentum the sun gave them when they were born five billion years ago."

Is the Dust-cloud theory scientifically true?

"All we can say is that it's the most reasonable idea we have today of what happened to give rise to our planetary system and to any others that might exist in the universe. What we can be absolutely certain of is that the sun and the planets are all members of the same family."

LIFE ON OTHER WORLDS

TO FIND A SUN LIKE OURS

One of the best things we can say about the Dust-cloud theory is that it offers us the strong possibility of life on other worlds.

If we believed that planets are the result of traffic accidents or similar disasters, then planetary systems would be rare animals. But if planets are born out of dust clouds, then there must be millions, even billions, of planetary systems right in our own galaxy. It would be impossible to imagine how many there must be in the entire universe.

And if other planetary systems circling around other suns, why not other planets like our earth? It was disappointing to learn that the chances of life on the other planets of our solar system are so poor. But now think of all the possibilities of life on the planets of billions of stars.

And if there is life, who knows but that on some of these planets there may be creatures very much like us. We begin with the history of our solar system and soon find ourselves on the trail of intelligent life among the stars.

Locate a star like our sun and you may come upon a planetary system like ours with perhaps an earth like ours.

Big question: How to find such stars?

You might say, "Simple enough. Just look for them with the help of powerful telescopes."

Unfortunately, no telescope, no matter how large or powerful, can make out the presence of planets outside our solar system.

And it is not because they are so small and far away. It is chiefly because the light of a star would overwhelm the light of a nearby planet. For much the same reason, we cannot see the planets of our own sun during the day. Our star drowns out their light.

Well now, if we can't see the planets of other stars, how are we to locate them?

We could place a star under close watch to see if anything is disturbing its motion. All heavenly bodies react to anything in their vicinity. The star 61 Cygni, we know, is not moving the way a well-behaved star should. Something is interfering with its movement through the heavens.

Can it be another star? Probably not. Whatever is bothering 61 Cygni is not much heavier than Jupiter. We are therefore inclined to think that 61 Cygni has one or more planets of its own.

As you see, this is hardly a very satisfying way of discovering planets outside our solar system.

What we shall do, instead, is try to reason out the existence of such planets. We'll begin by saying that since our star has its own planetary family, there must be many other stars that have their own family.

Of course, not any old star will do.

We'll leave out stars that give off very little heat. Life likes to be kept warm.

Neither will we pay any mind to stars that live only a few million years and then give up. Life requires a star that stays in business a good long time. It took something like five billion years before man appeared in our solar system. And it probably would take that long for a manlike creature to develop near another star. Life must have time to make many experiments, some of which are bound to fail. We want a really long-lasting star.

We'll also omit the binaries—and they take in almost half the stars in the sky. Life becomes impossible when a planet has to adjust to two—and sometimes more—stars.

Which stars then are the most likely candidates for planet families of their own?

Those about the same size and brightness as ours.

Those having the same kind of materials as ours.

And those that have been shining about the same length of time.

But when we have located these stars—and there are many of them—how will we know we are on the right track? Aren't we just guessing?

We might be—except for this amazing fact: The stars that answer these three tests are all slowpoke stars. Check their light through the spectroscope, and you will discover that they are all turning slowly on their axis *just like the sun*!

At once we are struck by a thought: Whatever is stalling the sun's spin is doing the same thing to these stars. And we know what slowed down the sun! These stars must have given up a good share of their momentum to a planetary family of their own. There seems to be no other reasonable explanation.

"It's not by chance," says Fred Hoyle, the Steady-state astronomer, "that stars that resemble the sun spin slowly. Like the sun, they have their own planets."

At one time, we thought that life could only be found here on earth. Now we are convinced that it is scattered, not only throughout our galaxy, but also throughout the other galaxies of the universe.

Let's suppose a distant star does have its own planets. Does that mean they bear life? Maybe conditions are unfavorable for life. Maybe these planets are too close to their star or too far away. After all, we here on earth are pretty fortunate. We are just the right distance from the sun to maintain life comfortably. Imagine our planet if it was twice that distance from the sun. Not much chance of life then!

There'd be no life on such a planet—at least not for the present. But what of the future? You'll recall that our star, like other stars, is getting hotter.

Someday the twice-the-distance-from-the-sun "earth" would be quite warm enough for life. We just happen to be on a planet where conditions for living are good now—lucky us. Someday we may be very sorry we are not on that far-off earth.

In any planetary system we can expect life to pop up sooner or later.

Throughout the length and breadth of the universe there are worlds where life is now in existence, others where life once existed and has since passed away, and still others where life will one day be born.

OTHER WORLDS AND OTHER MEN

The prospects for finding life outside our solar system seem to be very good. We expect to discover, on a planet of a distant star, forms of life resembling bacteria, toadstools, mosses, or even insects. But what about finding a creature like man, a being who is as eager to communicate with us as we are with him!

Well, let's see. If we say that the coming of man was just accidental, then the chances of his ever having happened are one in many billions. It is not likely that we'll ever find him on any other planet in the universe. We might as well stop looking right now.

But suppose we say, instead, that man is a normal, natural development on this planet. Once you have the kind of planet ours is, man or something very much like him will appear sooner or later. In that case it is likely that man—or his reasonable facsimile—will also show up on planets that closely resemble the earth.

In other words, what happens in one place will eventually happen in every other place where conditions are the same.

But will the higher creatures on far-off planets look like man?

It is not unlikely. Man's appearance is probably no accident either. We would not willingly exchange our shape, posture, size, or even our teeth, for those of any other creature, real or imaginary. We recognize the great advantages in two hands with flexible fingers; two feet on which to stand, walk, and run; a pair of eyes five or six feet off the ground to spy out the surrounding country; and a head with armor of bone to enclose our brain.

87

Nature has given us no monopoly on such features. She undoubtedly uses her successful models again and again. This does not mean that Nature cannot improve on us. Four legs are probably better than two—somewhere there may be intelligent beings resembling centaurs.

We can reasonably expect to find manlike creatures in other parts of the universe. The only trouble is that we will never meet them face to face. The vastness of space will always keep us from dropping in on one another.

But what of the stars that are quite close to us? Shouldn't we hope to become acquainted with the inhabitants of their planets?

Let's try our closest neighbor star, Alpha Centauri.

Sorry, we are wasting our time! It's about the age of our sun, so there's been enough time for life to develop; however, it's part of a binary, and that lets Alpha Centauri out altogether.

There are forty other stars within 16 light-years of us, and only two, Tau Ceti and Epsilon Eridani, meet the conditions for life.

Even if a Tau Ceti spaceman took it into his head to pay us a surprise visit, he'd be discouraged before he had gone very far. The trip would take hundreds of thousands of years. Not surprising that we've had no callers from the outside.

Communication, however, is certainly possible. Someday we will have the technical know-how for exchanging messages with beings who live hundreds of light-years away.

Is it possible to figure out how many worlds would like to get in touch with us? On how many planets are there creatures as curious and as adventurous as we are?

First, let us try to estimate how many planets in the universe hold the possibilities of life.

We'll start with our galaxy.

Ten percent of the stars are, like our sun, slow spinners.

We'll venture that most of these slow spinners have given up part of their momentum to a family of planets. If there are a hundred billion stars in our galaxy—and there are probably many more—then ten billion are tied to planetary systems.

Let's say that each of the slow stars is accompanied by five planets. That gives us a total of 50 billion planets. Now we'll imagine that one out of fifty holds life. After all, in our solar system one out of nine supports life, so our figures are very modest. We are now down to a billion planets with the possibilities of life.

On how many of this billion has life evolved into some sort of higher creature? Your guess is as good as mine. Let's say one out of five hundred. Is that too much? All right, we'll say, one out of a thousand.

So we end up with a million planets, in our galaxy alone, with creatures as intelligent as we are—and probably many of them are *more* intelligent.

Now if we should multiply the number of galaxies in the universe by this figure, we would have billions of planets inhabited by manlike beings.

Higher life is probably scattered through the length and breadth of the universe. And here we have been saying that the universe is a lonely place!

We certainly are not alone.

THE EARTH

THE EARTH IN SPACE

We began our history of the universe with the story of the stars and the galaxies. We then turned to our own solar system. Now we investigate what for us is the most important of the heavenly bodies—the earth.

What does the earth look like? For a few moments let us see it, not as our home, but as one of the nine planets of the solar system. We'll imagine we are viewing it from Mars, 50 million miles away.

Our first thought would be that two planets, not one, are flying in the earth's orbit around the sun. The earth and the moon look like companion planets circling about each other. We might suppose, as a few astronomers have, that the moon is not a satellite but another planet that the earth once captured. If that is the case, then the earth and moon are the only double planets in the solar system.

To us on Mars, the earth would be—aside from the sun— the brightest and most beautiful object in the skies. Through our telescope, we'd make out the white polar caps at the North and South Poles, the blue oceans, and the vast land masses covered with green vegetation. We'd see the clouds floating across the sky.

Checking the movement of the earth, we'd discover that it

turns around on its axis once every twenty-four hours. "Does the earth's spin give it a bulge around the middle?" we'd wonder.

The earth does have a very slight bulge. The diameter from the North to the South Pole is 7,900 miles. The diameter at the equator is 7,927 miles; a difference of only twenty-seven miles keeps the earth from being a perfect sphere. In the Arctic, you'd be about thirteen miles closer to the center of the earth than you would be in the tropics.

When the earth was young—and softer than it is today—the material around the equator had a tendency to fly off into space. You probably had the same feeling when you were at the end of a row of skaters playing "Crack-the-Whip"—you may have been thrown off the line by the force of the spin. But the earth's material, aided by gravitation, held on and just bulged. The earth's crust then hardened over the bulge.

After further observation of the earth, we on Mars would probably decide that the chances of life on earth are excellent.

The twenty-four-hour spin indicates that the earth does not get too hot or too cold as do Mercury and Venus.

The clouds floating across the earth's sky point to the presence of considerable amounts of water vapor. The green surface of the planet informs us that there must be plenty of vegetation. And vegetation indicates free oxygen and an atmosphere containing other gases also.

To hold the atmosphere captive, the earth must have a relatively high surface gravity. It must, therefore, have an unusually large mass. How massive is it? The amount of matter in a planet can be figured out by determining the gravitational pull between it and a nearby body, such as a moon.

If we Martian astronomers knew the method of calculation, we'd be aware that the earth has a mass of sixty-six hundred billion billion tons (6,600,000,000,000,000,000,000). A globe of water the same size as the earth would weigh five and a half times less.

It would not take us very long to figure out that it is impossible for the inside of the earth to be filled with water, and it certainly can not be filled with gases as the outer planets are. Whatever occupies the inside of the earth must be good and heavy.

A LAKE OF IRON

DEEP INSIDE THE EARTH

One of the most mysterious planets in the solar system is, strangely enough, the earth. We know very little about our own home in space.

It is true we know quite a bit about the surface on which we live. But just below us lie 8,000 miles of unexplored territory —the interior of the planet. Like the insects that spend their lives skimming the water of the pond, we are surface creatures unaware of the secrets below us.

What is the interior of the earth like?

We suppose it must be like what we see all about us: water, sand, soil, rock, metals, coal, and whatever else comes out of mines. But what we are describing is only the crust of the earth. The crust is a hard, cool outer shell no more than 3 to 25 miles deep, as thin proportionately as the skin on an apple.

The rest of the earth cannot be anything like the crust!

How do we know? The deepest mines go down only a mile or two, and the deepest oil wells only four miles. Yet we are positive that the earth below us is different from what we see around us.

Well, we do know how much the earth weighs. If it were made of the materials we find on the surface, it would weigh only half as much.

Here's a pretty how-do-you-do! How to solve it?

Only by imagining that whatever is inside the earth is so heavy that it more than makes up for all the light material on the crust.

How can we find out what is inside?

There are a number of ways. For one thing, the earth is part of the solar system. We wouldn't expect it to be too different from the other small planets. If we could, just for a moment, peer into one of them, we'd probably learn a great deal about our own.

Many astronomers think that meteorites are.fragments of a planet that broke up a long time ago. Examine a meteorite, they say, and you'll get a fine view of the inside of a planet.

Now some meteorites are made of iron and some of stone. Our guess, therefore, is that the inside of our planet consists of stone and iron.

Fortunately, we have much more direct evidence of what the interior of the earth is like.

We know that the pressure inside the earth equals millions of tons per square inch. We need go only half a mile beneath the surface for visible evidence. The walls of a mine shaft bulge in; the stone floor buckles upward. Wooden beams shatter like toothpicks. The squeezed rock almost refuses to release the miner's drill.

The farther down you go, the greater grow the temperature and pressure. Finally the hardest stone flows like liquid. When a volcano erupts, it brings to the surface rock that has been turned to mud in the hot interior of the earth. Our planet, so firm and hard on the surface, is soft within.

The most accurate information we have about the inside of the earth comes to us indirectly, through the study of earthquakes.

Earthquakes occur when rocks beneath the crust crack and

96

slip. Vibrations set up by such slipping reach the surface, where they cause tremendous damage. The earthquake of 1755 in Portugal destroyed the city of Lisbon and killed 60,000 of the population.

Earthquake waves also travel away from the surface. By the time they come up on the other side of the earth, they've lost all their "punch."

Many thousands of miles from where they started, these waves are picked up by a seismograph, a delicate instrument that detects their presence somewhat the way a radio set picks up radio waves.

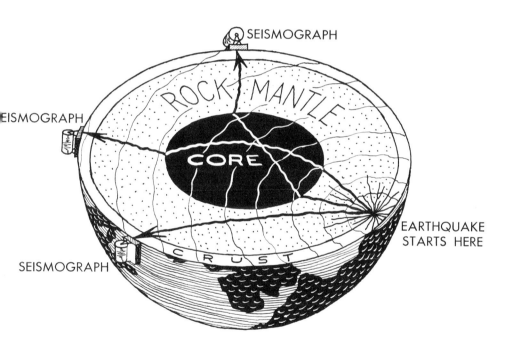

When earthquake waves pass from one material into another—from rock into liquid, for instance—they change speed and direction. The bending of these waves, detected by seismographs, helps us to map the earth's interior.

The seismograph allows us to accompany earthquake waves right through the earth. These waves don't travel in straight paths; they change both their speed and their direction every time they enter another kind of material. The seismograph records these changes and shows us whether a wave is passing through a solid or a liquid.

After tracing the paths of many thousands of these waves, we begin to "see" the inside of the earth a little more clearly.

On the surface is the thin crust on which we live. Under it is a mantle of very heavy rock 2,000 miles thick. This mantle floats on a strange lake 4,000 miles deep. It is a lake of liquid iron. Or perhaps it is a mixture of iron and nickel. (The metallic meteorites are a combination of iron and nickel.)

Now at last we understand why the earth is so heavy: It has a heart of iron!

How did the earth ever come to arrange itself into such a neat package: a kind of jelly-iron center, a thick cover of soft stone, and then a thin skin.

Did the core form first? Did the stone mantle then wrap itself around the iron? And finally did the crust stretch over all of it? It hardly seems likely.

When the earth condensed out of that dust cloud, it was probably a cold mixture of iron, stone, and light materials. A rain of matter from what was left of the dust cloud kept increasing the size of the earth. As it grew bigger, its pressure went up and so did its temperature. Finally the entire earth melted and became a ball of flowing lava.

The heavier materials sank to the bottom and the lighter ones rose to the top. Most of the iron was deposited in the center and formed the core. The rock rested above it and formed the mantle. The lightest matter floated to the top and became the crust.

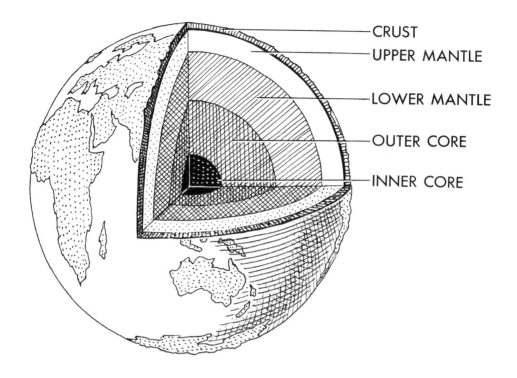

CRUST
UPPER MANTLE

LOWER MANTLE

OUTER CORE

INNER CORE

The interior of the earth is made up of a series of layers, each composed of different materials. The mantle is probably made of molten rock, and the core is probably iron and nickel in a highly dense, liquid state.

Are we certain that this is the way our earth was shaped? We will be certain only when we know much more than we do today about what lies just beneath our feet. It is curious, but we are more aware of what is happening on distant stars than we are of what is happening inside our own planet. We will probably get to distant planets before we discover a way to penetrate to the center of our own planet, only a few thousand miles away.

THE SURFACE OF THE EARTH

About three billion years ago, the rain of material from the dust cloud ended. The earth cooled off, the rocks solidified, and the crust of the earth hardened.

From here on in, you might think, the history of the earth should be simple to follow. After all, the surface is an open book to us. Unlike the interior it is not hidden by billions of tons of rock and metal. We've measured and weighed it. We've scaled its mountains. We've plumbed its oceans and seas. We spend our lives on it. We certainly ought to know it.

Unfortunately for our hopes, the earth we see today is not the earth of three billion years ago or even one hundred thousand years ago.

The earth's surface has been in constant change ever since the day it was created. What today is jungle was once desert. What is now highland was once valley. What was once mountain is now the bottom of the ocean. No wonder we come across fossilized oyster shells on mountain peaks.

As late as two hundred thousand years ago, North America and Europe were covered by jungles through which tigers and elephants roamed. Ice stretched over a good part of India and South America.

At one time Alaska was warm enough to hold dense forests. Under the frozen soil we find their remains today in the form of coal. In the past the Petrified Forest was really a forest. Today it is a desert.

The earth changes all the time.

Even the ocean has shifted. We find traces of it thousands of miles inland. In the Blue Ridge Mountains you'll come on rock made of limestone. Ages ago this region was covered by the sea, and the remains of tiny coral-like sea creatures built the stone you now sit on. Even the high Himalayas in India were once under the waves of the ocean.

Sometimes we can witness important changes in the surface of the earth within our own lifetime.

One day in 1943 a farmer in Central Mexico was amazed to see a wisp of smoke rising from a crack in his cornfield. Soon lava came pouring out. Within a few days he had a steaming volcano on his land, and within a few years a great mountain which we call Paracutin.

Some of the highest mountains in the world have been created by volcanic action: Fujiyama in Japan, Mount Kilimanjaro in Africa, and Mount Rainier in Washington.

Let us try to imagine what the earth looked like a long time ago.

If a giant were to slide North and South America across the Atlantic, they would interlock very nicely with the edges of Europe and Africa, very much like the pieces of a jigsaw puzzle.

Is that an accident? Or does it reveal the way the continents were once arranged?

Notice that, with the American continents pulled over to Europe and Africa, the Pacific Ocean area becomes tremendous.

Now let's ask our jigsaw-playing giant to pluck the moon out of the sky and set it down in the enlarged Pacific.

Fits very neatly, doesn't it?

Again just an accident? Or shall we guess that at one time before the earth cooled off, the moon was a part of our planet and that all the continents were bunched together in one great land mass?

Once the moon flew off to its proper place in the sky, the continents began to drift apart, floating over the smooth crust of the globe like cakes of ice over water until they reached their present geographical positions, where they settled down.

Is this theory of drifting continents true? We really don't think so today. It may solve a jigsaw puzzle but it hardly fits the facts. The earth does not yield her secrets that easily.

Recent exploration of the sea bottom indicates that the floor is not smooth at all. Even under the oceans, the crust is made of heavy rock, including mountains that rise up six thousand feet under the waves of the Atlantic. Hardly a gliding surface for continents!

Another drifting continent theory suggests that the molten material beneath the crust is in a state of slow convection. That is, it is turning over like water heated in a pot. Such convection currents move up and then sideways, and as they do, so the theory goes, they carry the continents along with them.

We can only guess that the continents once formed a single great land mass, but we can be certain that they have been linked together at various times.

In the last million years ice has crept down from the Arctic four times and covered a good part of the earth. At times almost one third of the globe was blanketed by glaciers, some of them a mile high. On the American continent the ice flowed as far south as Missouri, Illinois, and Indiana, and a solid wall of ice higher than the tallest skyscraper covered what is now New York City. Only about 25,000 years ago did the last ice sheet slowly retreat to the north.

The glaciers of the ice age transformed the surface of the earth. In some places their weight was so great that the earth sank beneath them. But their most spectacular effect was to link the continents.

By storing the water that would otherwise have found its way back to the sea, the glaciers lowered the level of all the oceans of the world. A tremendous amount of water is locked in glaciers even today. If the glaciers of Greenland and the Antarctic were to melt suddenly, the present ocean level would rise three hundred feet, thereby destroying many of the world's largest cities.

As the glaciers grew during the ice age, the level of the seas dropped anywhere from 125 to 800 feet. Vast new tracts of land rose out of the water.

A good part of the Mediterranean Sea was drained off, and Africa and Europe were joined together in several places. A land bridge linked England with the rest of the European continent. Australia became a part of Asia.

Out of the Bering Sea, in the Far North, appeared a great land area that tied northeastern Asia to Alaska. Over this spacious avenue, about 1,300 miles wide, the animals and plants of the Old World found their way to the New World. Mammoth, mastodon, elk, moose, camel, bear, wolf, and horse came to America over this dry-land route.

Long before the first European navigators sailed westward across the broad Atlantic, men, women, and children had walked eastward from Asia to America. The discoverer of America was not Columbus but a bold Mongolian wanderer from Siberia, ancestor of all the American Indians.

The glaciers melted four times during the ice age. The water returned to the sea, and the great land bridges sank beneath the waves. Each period of ice advance and ice retreat took hundreds of thousands of years.

We are living during the period of the latest retreat. Will the ice return? Will the lands now sunk beneath the waves rise again? One thing we can be certain of: The earth changes.

The earth changes, but very slowly.

The Alps have grown taller, but by no more than the height of a pencil stub since the days of Julius Caesar. The oceans

The Himalayan Mountains in a photograph taken by astronaut Gordon Cooper—not by an outer-space astronomer—during his 22-orbit swing around the earth on May 18, 1963.

climb up on the coast or fall back, but only a foot or two every hundred years.

It was at least a billion years after its birth before the earth melted and the iron seeped down to the core. Another billion went by before the earth cooled enough for life to begin. For another billion years or so life gradually changed from the simplest forms to that of the worms. Only in the last two billion years have warm-blooded creatures evolved. Man came to this planet less than two million years ago.

You must be patient with our earth; it takes its time.

SANDPAPERING THE GLOBE

EROSION SHAPES THE EARTH

The earth is never still!

Each day of every year, wind, rain, hail, sleet, and snow beat ceaselessly against its surface.

By day, the heat of the sun expands the rocks. At night, they contract. Swelling and shrinking, they crack and loosen. Finally they fall and, in falling, shatter other rocks below.

The rain fills every tiny pore in the rock. When winter comes, the water turns to ice, expands, and rips open the biggest boulders.

In the spring, glaciers start their slow, awesome journey down to the lowlands. They carry huge stones that scrape against the sides of the mountains like the roughest sandpaper.

In time jagged peaks smooth down and rugged mountains become gentle slopes. Look at a mountain and its shape will tell you its age. Smoothly rounded mountains like the Appalachians are very old. The Rockies with their toothlike peaks are young.

Waterfalls cut deep ravines and gorges through the moun-

The surface of the earth is under constant attack by the elements. One furious wind- and rainstorm ripped open a level field near Natrium, West Virginia, in 1950 and left this gorge behind—320 feet long, 100 feet wide, and 60 feet deep.

tains and widen the valleys. Boulders carried by swift mountain streams gnaw and rip at the shore.

Polished by constant rubbing, the boulders become stones. Stones become gravel, and gravel is finally beaten into fine sand. With the coming of plants, gravel and sand turn into rich soil.

Rivers are constantly relocating the land. Every moment in the day, they transport huge portions of our planet's surface from the mountains down into the plains.

The Nile River rises in the mountains of Abyssinia and flows north for thousands of miles before it reaches the flatlands of

Egypt. The soil that the Nile takes from the mountains of Abyssinia is deposited on the plains of Egypt. Every thousand years, Egypt grows three feet higher.

Once upon a time the surface of this planet was all hard, dead rock. The forces of nature ground it up and prepared the way for the formation of the soil. Without erosion, life could never have appeared on the earth.

FOUNTAINS OF LIFE

AIR AND WATER

How did life happen to come to this planet?

Could it just as well not have happened? Was it only chance that brought together the essential chemicals and set them going?

Many astronomers believe that chance played only a small part. That life should come was no more an accident than that the planets should circle the sun.

Things don't just happen in the universe. They develop, step by step, in an orderly way. If there is a dust cloud, you may be confident that a planetary family will be born. If there is a planet like the earth, you may be pretty sure that life will come into existence on it—sooner or later.

Life came to this planet because the conditions for living were right.

Life requires a nearby star from which to draw its energy. The temperature of the star must be neither too low or too high. If our sun's heat dropped only 13 percent, the earth would soon be covered with a blanket of ice a mile thick. If the sun's heat rose 30 percent, all life here would be destroyed.

The spin of a planet on which life exists must be fast enough to scatter the star's heat evenly. If our day were twenty-four days long, instead of twenty-four hours, we'd freeze on the dark side and broil on the light.

The planet must be heavy. If it is too light, it cannot hold an atmosphere. Because of our heavy iron core, the gravitational pull of the earth is strong enough to keep the air close to us.

As far as we know, life demands a plentiful supply of oxygen. On Mars and Venus, most of the oxygen was drawn out of the atmosphere and combined with metals. But on earth, green plants and trees constantly renew the supply. Every year they add 400 million tons of oxygen to the air. One fifth of the earth's atmosphere is oxygen.

We live at the bottom of a sea of air that extends 600 miles or more into space. The weight of the air directly above each of us is equal to that of a dozen heavy refrigerators. Why, then, don't we collapse under it?

Because the pressure inside us exactly equals that of the atmosphere pressing down on us. The pressure inside your body is so great that if you suddenly shot up into space, say 200 miles above the earth, your eyes would pop and your insides leak out like an overripe tomato. In the same way, fish living at the bottom of the sea burst when brought up to the surface. We too are "bottom" creatures.

Oxygen is an all-purpose ingredient for life. We breathe it in order to live. We also, in a way, drink it. Combined with two parts of hydrogen, oxygen magically becomes H_2O, or water.

Life demands water. We stay wet in order to survive. Water is part of every living cell. Compared to a jellyfish, which is 97 percent water, man is a dry creature. Nevertheless he is 75 percent water. Even his bones are 20 percent water.

Life is really water into which a few minerals have been dropped. Every cell in our body is a solution of various substances in water.

Water is all about us—in the rivers, the seas, the soil, and the air. Three fifths of the earth is covered by water. A Martian visitor would probably describe our planet to his long-eared relatives back home as a sphere of water out of which islands rise.

Life was born in the sea, and when the first animals came up on the land they locked up within themselves the salt water from which they came. Every one of us carries the mark of the sea within our bodies.

Watery ourselves, we live on a watery globe. We could not live if we failed to renew our supply of water from the tremendous reservoir the earth provides.

We begin to see why life has been so successful on this earth. It meets all of life's basic demands.

Life will probably answer an invitation from any planet where conditions are as good.

A WORLD OF THE DEAD

THE MOON

What would the earth be like without water and air?

Probably like the moon!

The moon is a world without wind, cloud, or rainbow, seas, or lakes. There is not enough moisture to set one grass seed growing, nor air enough to fill a caterpillar.

Without air the moon is a world without sound, for sound needs a medium to travel through. You could hear neither a voice in the distance nor a rifle shot under your nose.

Without an atmosphere the surface of the moon goes through extremes of heat and cold. At high noon of the two-week-long moon day, the rocks are as hot as boiling water. When the long night comes, they fall to the temperature of dry ice.

Expose your bare palm to the sun. Your palm burns while the back of your hand freezes in the shade.

The moon has no atmosphere because it is so small and light.

Fifty moons could fit within the space of our planet. The moon is a featherweight with a surface gravity six times less than that of the earth.

When the moon was ripped off the floor of the Pacific—if that is the way it was created—all it could carry away was the light rock lying just under the crust of our planet. It missed the iron, which had already sunk to the center of the earth.

Unlike the earth, the moon today is what it was billions of years ago. The air and water which give us life have transformed the surface of our planet again and again. But the moon has never been touched by change. Its history is written all over its face.

Part of the moon's story is told by its craters. Look at the moon through a telescope and you will see what seem to be the craters of volcanoes—then the moon is not a dead body! It must be bubbling with volcanic activity.

But before we get excited, let us examine these craters carefully. They are nothing like the craters of volcanoes here on earth.

When lava spills over the sides of a volcano, it builds a mountain. If you wanted to look into the crater of Mount Etna or Mount Vesuvius, you'd have to climb several thousand feet above sea level.

But suppose you were exploring a crater on the moon. After climbing up to the edge, you'd have to clamber down twice as far to reach the floor of the crater. The craters of the moon are below ground level.

If the moon craters are not volcanoes, what are they?

Right here on earth we have craters that look like those on the moon: the holes left by falling meteorites. What we see on the moon are the scars left by objects that fell out of the sky a long time ago.

After it tore itself free of the earth—assuming that it ever

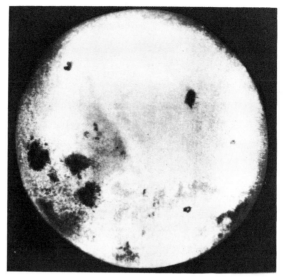

(Top) In October, 1959, a Russian automatic space station circling the moon brought back mankind's first view of the far side of our satellite. *(Bottom)* The surface of the moon is rugged, with cracks as deep as the Grand Canyon and mountains higher than Mount Everest. One of the largest craters, Copernicus, is surrounded by a wall 12,000 feet tall at its highest point. The dark areas in this photograph are maria, or large plains.

was a part of the earth—the moon was in a semisoft state. Dust-cloud material still filled the heavens and continued to rain down on the moon.

When the rain stopped, the scars were left behind and hardened. That is probably why the moon looks like a ball of clay that has been punctured by thousands of pellets.

The earth was hit by the same kind of bombardment. But the action of wind and rain long ago erased all trace of the attack.

The earth keeps its secrets. The moon, like a gossipy neighbor, gives them away.

The moon seems to say: "Don't be too proud. If it weren't for water and air, you'd look just like me."

THE FIRST TIME IT RAINED

HOW THE EARTH BEGAN

Little by little, we are getting a better picture of how the earth began. The evidence that science has been collecting from the stars, the moon, the meteorites, and the interior of our planet tells one clear, consistent story.

Because there is no direct proof, men will continue to argue and change their theories from time to time. But with increasing knowledge, we grow more certain that we are on the right track.

We begin our story about five billion years ago, when a blob of dust and gas was tossed into space by a dust cloud. For us it is the most important event in the history of the universe, for the blob eventually became the earth on which we live.

For millions of years the embryo earth circled around the sun, cooling off and scooping up chunks of material that continued to rain out of the dust cloud.

The earth grew larger and larger. And as it did, its pressure and temperature mounted. Finally the earth melted. The iron sank through the muddy rock to the center of the earth. The light stone floated to the top and became the crust.

At this point the earth was so soft that its surface rose and fell like the tides, and the equator bulged. The earth began to spin faster, and each day the tides of molten rock rose higher and higher. Until finally one day, the side of the earth facing the sun was ripped off and hurled into space.

At once it began to orbit around the earth, as it faithfully does to this day.

Between the continents of the earth were great hollows. But there was no water to fill them. The Atlantic and the Pacific and the other oceans were empty.

All the water of the seven seas was suspended high above the earth in clouds so thick that no light could get through. The world was in darkness. The earth waited for its first drop of rain.

Sometimes the blackness would be lighted by flaming rock hurled from thousands of volcanoes. Earthquakes continually disturbed the still half-molten earth. The planet surged and quivered like a trembling animal. There was no life because there was neither water nor sunlight.

At last, about three billion years ago, the clouds began to break up.

Picture the fall of the first drop of rain. It strikes the burning rock like water on a hot stove. It hisses, turns to steam and at once flies back into the air. But it returns again and again. Finally the rock is cooled enough so that the first puddle of water collects on the surface of the earth.

And now the rain begins in earnest, a rain such as the earth has never seen since. Without pause, the rain comes down for days, months, years, even centuries. No longer can the hot rock drive the water back into the atmosphere. The rain gathers in pools, in ponds, in lakes, and in rivers. The oceans receive their first water.

Under the pounding of the rain, the surface of the earth loses more and more heat. The crust cools and shrivels over the warmer mantle below. It shrinks, like a drying apple, into folds, wrinkles, and ridges.

The first mountain ranges rise. And at the same time, the first swift streams start to gnaw away at them, carrying off rock and boulder. Erosion that will one day change the whole face of the earth has begun.

Stone and gravel roll down the mountains, smoothing them and filling in the valleys below. The rivers dissolve the salty minerals in the rocks and carry them into the new-formed oceans.

More and more salt reaches the ocean. Heated by the burning sun, the ocean water rises in the air. Clouds carry it over the land, where it falls as rain. Year after year the oceans become saltier and saltier. The minerals of the mountains salt the seas of the world.

The mountains wear down and the earth is smoothed off. But the earth continues to cool, and the surface shrinks and shrivels again. New mountains rise to take the place of old ones.

There have been three great upheavals of the earth's crust, the last one less than one billion years ago. And probably when the mountains we know today are all worn down, others will rise to take their place.

The earth is a breeder of mountains.

HOW LIFE CAME TO THE EARTH

One day, in the still dimly lit tropic seas, life began.

Exactly how it happened we do not know. Perhaps in the next few years, when scientists are able to put life together in the laboratory, we will discover what went on.

About three billion years ago, the chemicals necessary for life came together under the right temperature, pressure, and light. These chemicals had been washed down out of the mountain rocks by the streams that fed the oceans. Life is the child of the mountain and the sea.

In the warm waters of the early ocean, the dividing line between the non-living mineral and the stuff of life broke down. The very first organisms learned to take nourishment out of their surroundings and to reproduce themselves. After many millions of years, they evolved into the bacteria and other microbes we know today.

Was this first life animal or plant? Probably neither. It never had a chance to decide. Plants need plenty of sunshine, and the sun had just begun to make its way through the thick clouds.

But a time did come when the sun broke through for longer and longer periods. Some of the new organisms discovered that the sun could be of great help to them if they stayed close to the surface. A green chemical called chlorophyll appeared in these surface dwellers. Now they were able to use the carbon dioxide in the air and the water of the sea to create their own nourishment. The energy of the sun, 93 million miles away, entered these tiny shreds of life and made them independent creatures.

Not too long afterwards, the organisms that had been left behind at the bottom of the sea discovered their own recipe for growing up quickly and staying healthy. They ate the new plants and became the world's first animals. Ever since that time all animals, whether protozoa, fish, or man, have lived on green plants either directly or indirectly.

The process of evolution took over. One-celled plants and animals banded together in colonies, and in the course of millions of years became algae, sponges, and jellyfish. Starfish, worms, and horseshoe crabs came into existence.

Each new kind of animal or plant arose from a change in an earlier form. Many hundreds of thousands of different kinds failed to survive and perished from the earth. Nature had plenty of time to produce the successful ones.

Though life teemed in the tropic seas, on land nothing stirred. No wonder: The face of the earth was naked rock. There were no trees, no grass, no soil.

But in Silurian times, about 350 million years ago, plants and then animals rose out of the sea and invaded the land.

The first plants to reach land were a kind of seaweed growing in shallow water. When the sea drew back, they clung to the bottom with long roots and found out that land-living was not too bad.

These first land-plants grew in cracks in the rock and helped to form soil. They took in carbon dioxide and released free oxygen into the atmosphere.

When there was a sufficient amount of oxygen in the air, animals were able to come up on land.

Our blood, our bones, and even our tears indicate that we are descended from animals that once lived in the sea. Our bones are made of lime, a reminder of the days when our ancestors swam in a sea rich in calcium. The salt content of our bodies is as high as that of the early oceans.

It must have been a tremendous feat for the first animals that tried living on land, somewhat as it would be if we tried to live on the moon.

Countless species must have made the attempt. A few managed to survive, and their ancestors have populated the earth.

Some of the early fish, similar to the lungfish of today, discovered the trick of living in shallow pools. When the water dried up, they developed air sacs which later became lungs. They were able to live out of the water part of the year and became the first amphibians, ancestors of frogs and salamanders.

Fins, in the course of time, became legs. The eggs were now ejected from the body and had large yolks to feed the young before they were hatched. Able to breathe and move on land easily, the amphibians eventually gave up the sea completely.

Some developed a tough, scaly skin, which kept the fluids in their bodies from drying up. Now they could go as far as they liked from the sea. They could even live in the desert far inland. So the reptiles were born, and for a time they took command of the entire earth.

Ferns and mosses grew on the land and, later, seed plants and trees. The earth was beginning to look as it does at the present time.

And then, about 120 million years ago, birds and small mammals appeared.

THE CHAIN OF LIFE

MAN JOINS THE UNIVERSE

Among the animals that appeared on earth seventy million years ago was one that resembled the tarsier of the East Indies. The tarsier is an insect-eating, tree-hopping little mammal about the size of a kitten; he has big, bug eyes, a short, stout body, tidy habits, and the rare talent of swiveling his head halfway around his neck.

Take a good look at him. He may well be the ancestor of the human race!

About two million years ago, scientists believe, a number of his big-brained, apelike relatives left the trees in which they had always lived and set up housekeeping on the ground. They walked upright, learned to use tools and their tongues, and gradually developed an intelligence superior to that of any other creature on earth. Just about 500,000 years ago, they became the first men.

The first organisms that swam in tropic seas and the human race are tied together by an unbroken chain of life that stretches back three billion years.

Man is as much a part of this planet as are the birds, the trees, the mountains, the oceans, and the continents. And because he is part of this planet, he is also part of the universe.

He is a miniature of the universe. The material of his bones, flesh, and blood is the substance of the galaxies. The physical laws that control his movements guide the course of the most distant stars.

He is warmed by the energy of the sun; he is held safely to this ball in space by the force of gravitation; he is nourished by elements that were born in nebulae and in the explosions of supernovas.

But man is more than just a part of nature. A new chapter in the history of the universe was written when man came into existence.

Comets, planets, stars, and even galaxies have no choice in what they do. Willy-nilly, they follow the rules that were laid down for them.

Man, on the other hand, can decide for himself. He can make things happen in the universe—for good or ill.

Having discovered how the stars manufacture light and heat, man employed the secret to develop thermonuclear energy. Finding out how planets and their moons move about in their orbits, he thrust satellites of his own creation into the sky.

118

The probing and exploration of space by mankind promises to increase our knowledge of the heavens as much as did the invention of the telescope. It offers to all the people living on this small planet an historical opportunity for the cooperative, peaceful exploration of the solar system and what lies beyond.

It is not surprising that so many of our ideas about the heavens and earth are still guesswork. The universe has been here for about eight to fifteen billion years—perhaps, as some astronomers say, forever. Man has been around for less than one million years. He is just a newcomer, a Johnny-come-lately.

In time many of the mysteries will be solved. The blank spaces in the history of the universe will begin to be filled in. We may yet know what lies in the distant regions beyond the farthest galaxies. We may even have a better picture of how this universe of ours all began.

AFTERWORD

Let's take one more glance at the stars. We look up at them yet we are among them, part and parcel of them, ourselves the inhabitants of a small globe in space, a satellite of a star weaving in and out among other stars.

How quiet and still the heavens seem! But all the universe, we know, is in ceaseless motion. Our planet whirls on its axis day and night, orbiting forever around the sun. The sun sails along in a caravan of stars, circling about the Milky Way while the whole galaxy takes flight at ever-increasing speeds to ever more distant regions of the sky.

Would you read the history of the universe? Then keep your eye on the stars. You need no time machine, for the stars will tell you what happened in the past. In the sky we see the universe as it was yesterday, last year, billions of years ago, and, probably, as it will be in the future.

Suns, planets, moons, and galaxies are born; they grow old; they die; but the universe remains the same. In the midst of change, the universe remains unchanged. No matter in what direction we turn our telescopes, we come upon worlds not too different from our own. A visitor from the farthest galaxy would not be a stranger in ours.

While we stand here under the starlit sky, other beings on worlds far from ours are looking up at their own firmament of stars, and wondering, no doubt, about their place in the plan of the universe.

Before we go, we wave a greeting across the immensity of time and space.

INDEX

Alpha Centauri, 78, 88
amphibians, 117
Andromeda, galaxy in (M 31), 2 (illus.),
    11, 12, 14-15, 54m (illus.)
Antares, 23
asteroids, 4, 35, 59-60
atmosphere of earth, 94, 108
    of Jupiter, 62
    of Mars, 56, 57, 58
    of Mercury, 52-54
    of Saturn, 63-64
    of Venus, 55

Barringer Crater, 73 (illus.)
Betelgeuse, 23
Biela's Comet, 70
Big Dipper (Great Dipper), 11, 78
binaries. *See* double stars
Brahe, Tycho, 27, 54k

Ceres, 59
Chamberlin, T. C., 77
chlorophyll, 115
comets, 67-71, 67 (illus.), 69 (illus.),
    71 (illus.)
continents, 101-102
Cooper, Gordon, 92, 104
Copernicus, Nicolaus, 12
Crab Nebula, 26-27, 54k (illus.)
craters, 54a (illus.,) 73 (illus.), 110, 111
    (illus.)
Cygnus, the Swan, 54f (illus.), 54k
    (illus.)

Deimos, 56
Dog Star. *See* Sirius
Doppler effect, 31
double stars (binaries), 78, 85
drifting continents, 101-102
dust, cosmic, 15
dust cloud, 54a, 54h (illus.), 80-83,
    82 (illus.), 98, 107, 112
dwarf stars, 24, 26 (illus.)

earth, beginning of, 112-114
    core of, 99 (illus.)
    crust of, 95
    erosion of, 105-107, 106 (illus.)
    gravitation of, 94-95
    in space, 49, 93-95
    interior of, 21, 95-99 (illus.)
    life on, 107-109, 115-119
    mantle of, 99 (illus.)
    pressure within, 21, 96
    shape of, 92 (illus.), 94
    surface of, 100-106 (illus.)
    weight of, 94-95
earthquakes, 96-97 (illus.), 113
eclipse of sun, 48 (illus.)
elements, 25 (illus.), 30, 38-39
energy of sun, 17-22, 18 (illus.), 115
Epsilon Eridani, 88
erosion, 105-107, 106 (illus.)
evolution, 116-117
Evolutionary theory, 37-40, 44
expanding universe, 29-32, 37, 42, 43

fossil fuels, 18 (illus.)

125

galactic clouds, 44
galaxies, age of, 36
　　defined, 7
　　local group, 29
　　movement of, 8
　　origin of, 42-44
　　position in space of, 13-14
　　runaway, 29-32
　　shapes of, 13
　　See illustrations, pp. 2, 9, 10, 54h, 54k, 54l, 54m, 54o, 54p
Galileo, 12, 62, 64
Gamow, George, 38-40
glaciers, 102-103, 105
gravitation, 17, 27-29, 30, 38
　　of moon, 110
　　of sun, 68, 113
Great Dipper. *See* Big Dipper
Great Nebula, 54b (illus.)
Great Red Spot, 54d (illus.)

Hale telescope, 11, 35 (illus.), 54b
Halley's Comet, 67 (illus.), 68, 69 (illus.), 70-71
helium, 19
Hermes, 59
Herschel, William, 12
Himalayas, 101, 104 (illus.)
Hoyle, Fred, 41-44, 86
Hubble, Dr. Edwin, 11, 12
hydrogen, 16, 19, 21, 22 (illus.), 25 (illus.), 28, 43, 79, 80

ice age, 102-103
interstellar gas, 80

Jeans, Sir James, 77
Jupiter, 4, 49, 54d (illus.), 60-63
　　moons of, 62

Kepler, Johannes, 27, 54k

Laplace, Pierre Simon de, 75-76
Lemaître, Georges, 37-38, 40, 41
life, 40, 50-51, 86-89, 105
　　conditions for, 86, 88, 107-109
　　of man on earth, 117-119
　　on earth, 115-117
　　on Mars, 57-58
　　on Mercury, 54
　　on Venus, 54-56
life zone, 58
light-year, 6

M 31 (galaxy), 2 (illus.), 12, 13, 14, 54m (illus.)
Magellan, Ferdinand, 13
Magellanic Clouds, 13, 14
main sequence, 26 (illus.)
man, 87-89, 105, 117-119
Mariner II, 55
Mars, 4, 56-58
　　life on, 54e (illus.), 57-58
　　polar caps of, 54e (illus.)
Mercury, 52-54, 53 (illus.)
Messier's Catalogue, 54h
meteorites, 35, 67, 72-74, 73
meteors, 67-71 (illus.)
Milky Way, 7-14, 9 (illus.), 54b (illus.), 54f (illus.)
Mira, 23
moon, 4, 34, 54a (illus.), 109-112, 111 (illus.)
moons, of Jupiter, 62
　　of Mars, 56
　　of Neptune, 66
　　of Saturn, 64
Mount Wilson Observatory, 11
mountains, 100-101, 104 (illus.), 105-106, 114

nebular hypothesis, 75-77
nebulas. *See* illustrations:
　　Crab Nebula, 54k
　　Dumbbell Nebula, 54b
　　Great Nebula in Orion, 54b
　　Lagoon Nebula, 54k
　　NGC 2403, *frontispiece*
　　North American Nebula, 54f
　　Ring Nebula, 54f
　　Rosette Nebula, 54o
　　Veil Nebula, 54k
Neptune, 65-66
New General Catalogue, 54k
Newton, Sir Isaac, 33, 63
Nile River, 106-107
nuclear fission, 25 (illus.)

Occam's Razor, 79
oceans, 33, 100-101, 102, 103, 113-114, 115, 116
Orion, nebula in, 54b (illus.), 80
oxygen, 55, 57-58, 108

Palomar Observatory, 11, 12, 35 (illus.), 54b
Perseids, 70
Phobos, 56

planetoids. *See* asteroids
planets, 36, 49-50, 51 (illus.)
  earth, 93-109, 99 (illus.), 106 (illus.),
    112-117
  Jupiter, 4, 49, 54d (illus.), 60-63
  life on, 50-52, 83-89, 112-118
  Mars, 4, 54e (illus.), 56-58
  Mercury, 52-54, 53 (illus.)
  Neptune, 65-66
  origin of, 40, 76-78, 79-83
  Pluto, 6, 65-66
  Saturn, 54d (illus.), 63-64
  Uranus, 65-66
  Venus, 54-56, 54d (illus.)
Pleiades, 54f (illus.)
Pluto, 6, 65-66
Proxima Centauri, 78
Pup, the, 78

radio telescopes, 15-16 (illus.)
radio waves, 15
red giants, 7, 20 (illus.), 22-23, 26
  (illus.), 36
red shift, 31
rings of Saturn, 54d (illus.), 64
Roche Limit, 59-60, 64
rocks, age of, 33-34

Saturn, 54d (illus.), 63-64
Schmidt telescope (telescopic camera),
  14, 54b
seismograph, 97-98, 97 (illus.)
shooting stars, 71 (illus.), 72
Sirius, the Dog Star, 6, 78
solar system, 49-52ff., 51 (illus.)
  birth of, 75-81, 82 (illus.)
Southern Cross, 13
space, 13-14, 15-16
space station, 111
spectroscope, 30-31, 85
spiral arms, 8, 14
star 61 Cygni, 84
stars, 5-16, 20 (illus.), 23-27, 25 (illus.),
  54b, 54f (illus.)
  age of, 36
  elements in, 30
  evolution of, 26 (illus.)
  sound of, 15
  spin of, 85-86
  temperature of, 30
  See also:
    Alpha Centauri
    Betelgeuse

    double stars
    dwarf stars
    Epsilon Aurigae
    Epsilon Eridani
    Mira
    New General Catalogue
    Pleiades
    Proxima Centauri
    red giants
    Sirius
    sun
    star 61 Cygni
    Tau Ceti
Steady-state theory, 41-44
sun, 5 (illus.), 7, 9, 17-24, 22 (illus.),
  54e (illus.)
  age of, 36
  eclipse of, 48 (illus.)
  energy of, 17-22, 18 (illus.), 115
  future of, 21-24
  in galaxy, 7-9
  origin of, 76-83
sunspots, 54e (illus.)
supernovas, 24-27, 26 (illus.), 38, 54k
  (illus.)

tarsier, 117
Tau Ceti, 88
Taurus, supernova in, 25
telescope, 11-12, 62
  Hale, 11, 35 (illus.), 54b
  Schmidt, 54b
thermonuclear reaction, 19, 21, 26
  (illus.)
Triton, 66

universe, 3, 10-16, 25
  age of, 32-36
  expanding of, 29-32
  origin of, 27-29ff., 37-45
uranium, 33-34
uranium clock, 34
Uranus, 65-66
Ussher, Bishop, 33

Venus, 54-56, 54d (illus.)
volcanoes, 21, 96, 110

water, 81, 105, 108

X-rays, 18

ylem, 38

ABOUT THE AUTHOR

Arthur S. Gregor was born in the Greenwich Village section of New York City and has lived in and around the area most of his life. He earned a Master's degree in English literature at Columbia University and then went on to teach at Cornell, in the elementary and junior high schools of New York City, and at Brooklyn Technical High School. He is presently the principal of Public School No. 2 in Manhattan, and each year directs the Lower Manhattan Science Fair. Mr. Gregor's other books for young people include *Time Out for Youth* and *A Short History of Science*.